Math Skills Practice & Apply: Grade 4

BY
STEVE DAVIS

COPYRIGHT © 2000 Mark Twain Media, Inc.

ISBN 1-58037-127-2

Printing No. CD-1349

Mark Twain Media, Inc., Publishers
Distributed by Carson-Dellosa Publishing Company, Inc.

Table of Contents

Table of Contents

Introduction

This book provides the students with several practice pages for each mathematical concept in order to enhance their understanding. All concepts are presented from easier to harder in an effort to ensure the student is provided with success prior to moving to the next stage. With success comes confidence, with confidence comes willingness to try, and thus the student learns.

The mathematical concepts of place value, addition, subtraction, multiplication, division, fractions, geometry, and metrics are all covered. A multiplication table for multiplication of 1 through 12 is provided for students to fill out and then maintain with their notebooks for future reference. A small glossary that covers the concepts presented in this book is provided for issue to students.

At the conclusion of most concepts covered are pages of word problems that require the students to apply what they have learned. These problems are based solely on the concept covered.

Place Value: *Place Value Introduction*

Students cannot add, subtract, multiply, or divide if they do not understand the concept of **place value**. Draw the place value diagram showing values from thousandths all the way up to hundred thousands as shown below.

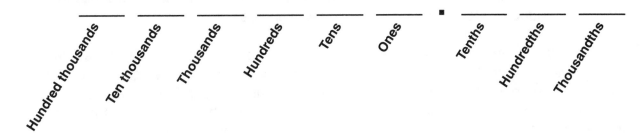

Now write 123,456.789 on the board. Ask the students how many hundred thousands are present. The answer is 1 because that is the number in the hundred thousands place. Continue with each place value.

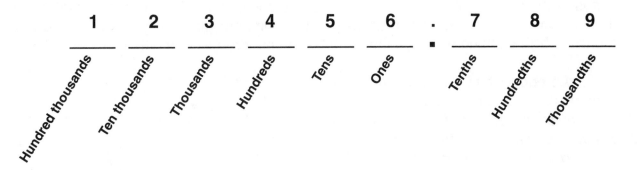

Now do the same thing with 952,381.047. Ensure the students fully understand that the number zero means there are no tenths in this number.

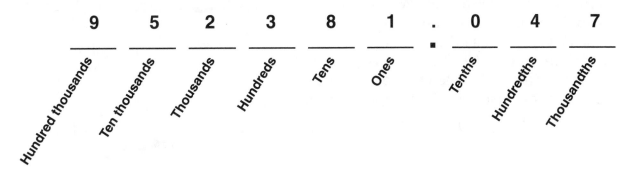

Place Value: *Place Value Introduction*

The next part of place value that needs to be covered is how to pronounce the numbers according to place value. The single most important concept is that the decimal point is pronounced as "and." Start out by telling the students that to pronounce the number, you must think in groups of three. The groups of three are: hundred thousands to thousands, hundreds to ones, and tenths to thousandths.

Have the students read this number: 583. They should read exactly "five hundred eighty-three." Do not let the students read only the digits such as "five eight three." Now write 583,000 on the board. Have the students read this number. They should have read exactly "five hundred eighty-three thousand." Point out that this number has thousand on the end because 583 was in the group of hundred thousands to thousands. Now write 0.583 on the board. Have the students read this number. They should have read "five hundred eighty-three thousandths." Once again thousandths was added to the end because 583 was in the group of tenths to thousandths.

Let's try combining the numbers. Write 250,369.718 on the board. Have the students identify the groups of three. They should identify 250 in the group of hundred thousands to thousands, 369 in the group hundreds to ones, and 718 in the group of tenths to thousandths. Have the students read the group of numbers individually. "Two hundred fifty thousand," "three hundred sixty-nine," and "seven hundred eighteen thousandths."

As long as the students keep the numbers in groups of three and place the word "and" in the decimal location, they will always pronounce the numbers correctly. Now, the decimal group needs to be covered in greater detail.

Write 0.230 on the board. Point out to the students that if a zero is on the right side of the number group, it is not pronounced. So this number would be "zero and twenty-three hundredths" and should be written as 0.23. Write 0.023 on the board. This number is "zero and twenty-three thousandths" because the zero is on the left of the number group. Write 0.200 on the board. This number is "zero and two-tenths" because the zeros are on the right side of the number group. It should be written as 0.2.

2

Name: _____ Date: _____

Place Value: *Place Value Practice #1*

Directions: For each problem below, identify how many of each place value is present.

	1) 263	2) 5,310.092	3) 204,509.100	4) 50.001
How many hundred thousands?				
How many ten thousands?				
How many thousands?				
How many hundreds?				
How many tens?				
How many ones?				
How many tenths?				
How many hundredths?				
How many thousandths?				

Directions: Identify the numbers according to the three groups for place value. The first one is completed for you.

	Hundred thousands to Thousands	Hundreds to Ones	Tenths to Thousandths
5. 587,230.040	587	230	40
6. 55,004.400			
7. 456.110			
8. 15.546			
9. 3,000			
10. 9.007			
11. 100,003.027			
12. 1,125.101			
13. 101,359.223			
14. 7,070.700			
15. 15,200.002			

Name: _____ Date: _____

Place Value: *Place Value Practice #2*

Directions: Write the number from the description given.

1. Sixty-seven and ninety-three thousandths _____

2. Eight hundred ten thousand nine hundred eleven and two hundred twenty-five thousandths _____

3. Zero and six thousandths _____

4. Five thousand six hundred twenty-one and twenty-one hundredths _____

5. Ninety-five thousand twelve and one hundred one thousandths _____

6. Two and two hundredths _____

7. Fifty-five and seventy-nine hundredths _____

Directions: Write out the value of each number.

8. 500,000 _____

9. 250 _____

10. 55 _____

11. 200,320.1 _____

_____

12. 6.25 _____

13. 0.045 _____

14. 43,001.01 _____

_____

15. 23.205 _____

Place Value: *Place Value Practice #2*

Addition: *Introduction*

There are two types of addition problems. The first type is called **no renaming** because the sum of the two numbers never exceeds nine. The second type is **renaming** because the sum of the two numbers equals ten or greater. Look at the addition table below. The answers in the shaded region are the no renaming sums, while the answers in the white region are the renaming sums. (This table is in the back of the book and should be copied onto an overhead plastic sheet for use with a projector.) Hand out the blank addition chart from the back of the book to the students and have them fill out the sums in each blank cell.

+	0	1	2	3	4	5	6	7	8	9
0	0	1	2	3	4	5	6	7	8	9
1	1	2	3	4	5	6	7	8	9	10
2	2	3	4	5	6	7	8	9	10	11
3	3	4	5	6	7	8	9	10	11	12
4	4	5	6	7	8	9	10	11	12	13
5	5	6	7	8	9	10	11	12	13	14
6	6	7	8	9	10	11	12	13	14	15
7	7	8	9	10	11	12	13	14	15	16
8	8	9	10	11	12	13	14	15	16	17
9	9	10	11	12	13	14	15	16	17	18

Write the problem 5 + 3 on the board. Using the overhead projector, show the students how to use the chart. Find the first number, 5, in the first row and highlight the entire column. Then find the second number, 3, in the first column and highlight the row. Where the highlighted row and column meet is the answer to the problem.

+	0	1	2	3	4	5	6	7	8	9
0	0	1	2	3	4	5	6	7	8	9
1	1	2	3	4	5	6	7	8	9	10
2	2	3	4	5	6	7	8	9	10	11
3	3	4	5	6	7	8	9	10	11	12
4	4	5	6	7	8	9	10	11	12	13
5	5	6	7	8	9	10	11	12	13	14
6	6	7	8	9	10	11	12	13	14	15
7	7	8	9	10	11	12	13	14	15	16
8	8	9	10	11	12	13	14	15	16	17
9	9	10	11	12	13	14	15	16	17	18

The answer is 8.

At this point, have the students complete the first and second addition practice sheets using the table.

Addition: *Introduction (continued)*

For two-digit and greater addition, place value combined with the table becomes extremely important. First, each problem should be lined up according to place value. Then the addition begins with the rightmost numbers and moves left.

Examples:

1. Write this problem on the board: 25 + 9. Have the students identify the ones, tens, hundreds, etc., for each number. Then line them up as follows:

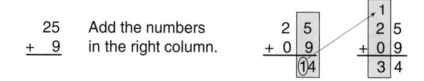

Since there is a number to the left of the 5 in 25, only the 4 of 14 can be used. The 1 must be carried to the next column above the 2 and then added to that column. This procedure would continue until there are no numbers to the left.

2. Write this problem on the board: 38 + 81. Now perform the steps listed above.

Since there are no numbers to the left, the 11 will remain as it is and the answer is 119.

3. Show this last example for the students.

Note that the second and third columns had to add three numbers.

Name: _____ Date: _____

Addition: *Addition Practice #1*

Directions: Find the sum of each problem using the addition table.

1. 5 + 4 = _____   2. 8 + 1 = _____

3. 3 + 4 = _____   4. 5 + 2 = _____

5. 1 + 8 = _____   6. 2 + 5 = _____

7. 9 + 0 = _____   8. 7 + 2 = _____

9. 0 + 5 = _____   10. 6 + 2 = _____

11. 7 + 1 = _____   12. 1 + 6 = _____

13. 2 + 1 = _____   14. 0 + 4 = _____

15. 4 + 4 = _____   16. 3 + 3 = _____

17. 2 + 7 = _____   18. 1 + 1 = _____

19. 6 + 0 = _____   20. 2 + 2 = _____

21. 7 + 0 = _____   22. 0 + 0 = _____

23. 5 + 3 = _____   24. 3 + 5 = _____

25. 3 + 1 = _____   26. 6 + 3 = _____

27. 1 + 4 = _____   28. 4 + 3 = _____

29. 0 + 7 = _____   30. 5 + 1 = _____

Directions: Find the sum of each problem using the addition table.

1.   2   2.   5   3.   7
   + 5   + 3   + 1

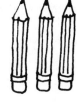

4.   3   5.   1   6.   9
   + 0   + 4   + 0

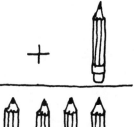

7.   4   8.   6   9.   8
   + 5   + 2   + 1

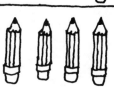

7

Name: _____ Date: _____

Addition: *Addition Practice #2*

Directions: Find the sum of each problem using the addition table.

1.   1 + 9 = 10

2.   5 + 6 = 11

3.   6 + 4 = 10

4.   3 + 9 = 12

5.   9 + 9 = 18

6.   4 + 8 = 12

7.   2 + 9 = 11

8.   7 + 7 = 14

9.   8 + 7 = 15

10.   9 + 2 = 11

11.   5 + 8 = 13

12.   6 + 6 = 12

13.   7 + 3 = 10

14.   8 + 3 = 11

15.   4 + 9 = 13

16.   2 + 8 = 10

17.   3 + 7 = 10

18.   8 + 6 = 14

19.   7 + 9 = 16

20.   4 + 7 = 11

21.   5 + 5 = 10

22.   7 + 5 = 12

23.   9 + 5 = 14

24.   4 + 6 = 10

25.   6 + 9 = 15

26.   5 + 7 = 12

27.   9 + 1 = 10

28.   6 + 8 = 14

29.   9 + 4 = 13

30.   3 + 8 = 11

Directions: Find the sum of each problem using the addition table.

1.   9
    + 5
    14

2.   7
    + 4
    11

3.   2
    + 9
    11

4.   5
    + 8
    13

5.   6
    + 7
    13

6.   4
    + 8
    12

7.   8
    + 8
    16

8.   7
    + 8
    15

9.   5
    + 6
    11

8

Name: _____ Date: _____

Addition: *Addition Practice #3*

Directions: Find the sum for each problem.

Example:

$$\begin{array}{r} 25 \\ + 9 \\ \hline \end{array}$$

Add the right numbers in the right column.

$$\begin{array}{r} 2\,5 \\ + 0\,9 \\ \hline 1\,4 \end{array}$$

$$\begin{array}{r} 1 \\ 2\,5 \\ + 0\,9 \\ \hline 3\,4 \end{array}$$

1. $\begin{array}{r} 35 \\ + 11 \\ \hline \end{array}$ 2. $\begin{array}{r} 91 \\ + 5 \\ \hline \end{array}$ 3. $\begin{array}{r} 62 \\ + 22 \\ \hline \end{array}$ 4. $\begin{array}{r} 51 \\ + 6 \\ \hline \end{array}$ 5. $\begin{array}{r} 15 \\ + 62 \\ \hline \end{array}$

6. $\begin{array}{r} 29 \\ + 30 \\ \hline \end{array}$ 7. $\begin{array}{r} 44 \\ + 51 \\ \hline \end{array}$ 8. $\begin{array}{r} 88 \\ + 1 \\ \hline \end{array}$ 9. $\begin{array}{r} 6 \\ + 82 \\ \hline \end{array}$ 10. $\begin{array}{r} 76 \\ + 12 \\ \hline \end{array}$

11. $\begin{array}{r} 7 \\ + 72 \\ \hline \end{array}$ 12. $\begin{array}{r} 90 \\ + 9 \\ \hline \end{array}$ 13. $\begin{array}{r} 51 \\ + 24 \\ \hline \end{array}$ 14. $\begin{array}{r} 67 \\ + 12 \\ \hline \end{array}$ 15. $\begin{array}{r} 86 \\ + 12 \\ \hline \end{array}$

16. $\begin{array}{r} 5 \\ + 73 \\ \hline \end{array}$ 17. $\begin{array}{r} 9 \\ + 50 \\ \hline \end{array}$ 18. $\begin{array}{r} 6 \\ + 41 \\ \hline \end{array}$ 19. $\begin{array}{r} 1 \\ + 88 \\ \hline \end{array}$ 20. $\begin{array}{r} 2 \\ + 81 \\ \hline \end{array}$

21. $\begin{array}{r} 33 \\ + 54 \\ \hline \end{array}$ 22. $\begin{array}{r} 37 \\ + 51 \\ \hline \end{array}$ 23. $\begin{array}{r} 49 \\ + 40 \\ \hline \end{array}$ 24. $\begin{array}{r} 57 \\ + 40 \\ \hline \end{array}$ 25. $\begin{array}{r} 20 \\ + 76 \\ \hline \end{array}$

26. $\begin{array}{r} 60 \\ + 25 \\ \hline \end{array}$ 27. $\begin{array}{r} 76 \\ + 23 \\ \hline \end{array}$ 28. $\begin{array}{r} 63 \\ + 33 \\ \hline \end{array}$ 29. $\begin{array}{r} 9 \\ + 20 \\ \hline \end{array}$ 30. $\begin{array}{r} 8 \\ + 11 \\ \hline \end{array}$

Name: _____ Date: _____

Addition: *Addition Practice #4*

Directions: Find the sum for each problem.

Example:

$$
\begin{array}{r} 526 \\ +\ 395 \\ \hline \end{array}
\qquad
\begin{array}{r} 52\ 6 \\ +\ 39\ 5 \\ \hline 1 \end{array}
\qquad
\begin{array}{r} 1 \\ 5\ 2\ 6 \\ +\ 3\ 9\ 5 \\ \hline 2\ 1 \end{array}
\qquad
\begin{array}{r} 1\ 1 \\ 5\ 2\ 6 \\ +\ 3\ 9\ 5 \\ \hline 9\ 2\ 1 \end{array}
$$

1.
$$\begin{array}{r} 321 \\ +\ 654 \\ \hline \end{array}$$

2.
$$\begin{array}{r} 525 \\ +\ 821 \\ \hline \end{array}$$

3.
$$\begin{array}{r} 654 \\ +\ 209 \\ \hline \end{array}$$

4.
$$\begin{array}{r} 489 \\ +\ 408 \\ \hline \end{array}$$

5.
$$\begin{array}{r} 101 \\ +\ 927 \\ \hline \end{array}$$

6.
$$\begin{array}{r} 156 \\ +\ 635 \\ \hline \end{array}$$

7.
$$\begin{array}{r} 257 \\ +\ 587 \\ \hline \end{array}$$

8.
$$\begin{array}{r} 853 \\ +\ 501 \\ \hline \end{array}$$

9.
$$\begin{array}{r} 128 \\ +\ 655 \\ \hline \end{array}$$

10.
$$\begin{array}{r} 863 \\ +\ 837 \\ \hline \end{array}$$

11.
$$\begin{array}{r} 952 \\ +\ 100 \\ \hline \end{array}$$

12.
$$\begin{array}{r} 901 \\ +\ 69 \\ \hline \end{array}$$

13.
$$\begin{array}{r} 650 \\ +\ 539 \\ \hline \end{array}$$

14.
$$\begin{array}{r} 999 \\ +\ 243 \\ \hline \end{array}$$

15.
$$\begin{array}{r} 666 \\ +\ 648 \\ \hline \end{array}$$

16.
$$\begin{array}{r} 577 \\ +\ 752 \\ \hline \end{array}$$

17.
$$\begin{array}{r} 25 \\ +\ 869 \\ \hline \end{array}$$

18.
$$\begin{array}{r} 8 \\ +\ 579 \\ \hline \end{array}$$

19.
$$\begin{array}{r} 956 \\ +\ 52 \\ \hline \end{array}$$

20.
$$\begin{array}{r} 607 \\ +\ 186 \\ \hline \end{array}$$

21.
$$\begin{array}{r} 9 \\ +\ 994 \\ \hline \end{array}$$

22.
$$\begin{array}{r} 907 \\ +\ 207 \\ \hline \end{array}$$

23.
$$\begin{array}{r} 95 \\ +\ 596 \\ \hline \end{array}$$

24.
$$\begin{array}{r} 76 \\ +\ 769 \\ \hline \end{array}$$

25.
$$\begin{array}{r} 7 \\ +\ 966 \\ \hline \end{array}$$

26.
$$\begin{array}{r} 87 \\ +\ 684 \\ \hline \end{array}$$

27.
$$\begin{array}{r} 139 \\ +\ 357 \\ \hline \end{array}$$

28.
$$\begin{array}{r} 931 \\ +\ 29 \\ \hline \end{array}$$

Name: _____ Date: _____

Addition: *Addition Practice #5*

Directions: Find the sum for each problem.

1. 4058 + 2045	2. 9015 + 6321	3. 5002 + 5297	4. 3571 + 1110
5. 5862 + 1057	6. 9542 + 200	7. 1287 + 533	8. 8347 + 9523
9. 1008 + 2068	10. 957 + 1008	11. 65 + 3808	12. 931 + 2009
13. 2583 + 2596	14. 6100 + 6304	15. 9467 + 1287	16. 10 + 9849
17. 2078 + 5222	18. 9 + 9867	19. 9800 + 54	20. 1067 + 577
21. 2495 + 96	22. 474 + 8530	23. 86 + 9463	24. 21 + 1394
25. 9003 + 525	26. 1365 + 57	27. 6571 + 78	28. 4848 + 8
29. 86 + 6886	30. 9 + 1568	31. 578 + 2057	32. 4 + 4988

11

Name: _____ Date: _____

Addition: *Addition Practice #6*

Directions: Find the sum for each problem.

1. $\begin{array}{r} 15896 \\ +\ 20547 \\ \hline \end{array}$	2. $\begin{array}{r} 95360 \\ +\ 15973 \\ \hline \end{array}$	3. $\begin{array}{r} 12571 \\ +\ 62730 \\ \hline \end{array}$	4. $\begin{array}{r} 35891 \\ +\ 10005 \\ \hline \end{array}$
5. $\begin{array}{r} 30045 \\ +\ 35570 \\ \hline \end{array}$	6. $\begin{array}{r} 57930 \\ +\ 84250 \\ \hline \end{array}$	7. $\begin{array}{r} 10570 \\ +\ 52749 \\ \hline \end{array}$	8. $\begin{array}{r} 90056 \\ +\ 65730 \\ \hline \end{array}$
9. $\begin{array}{r} 12593 \\ +\ 10004 \\ \hline \end{array}$	10. $\begin{array}{r} 67920 \\ +\ 20048 \\ \hline \end{array}$	11. $\begin{array}{r} 34765 \\ +\ 90070 \\ \hline \end{array}$	12. $\begin{array}{r} 67851 \\ +\ 80875 \\ \hline \end{array}$
13. $\begin{array}{r} 35426 \\ +\ 5790 \\ \hline \end{array}$	14. $\begin{array}{r} 60049 \\ +\ 867 \\ \hline \end{array}$	15. $\begin{array}{r} 90000 \\ +\ 8967 \\ \hline \end{array}$	16. $\begin{array}{r} 5555 \\ +\ 30493 \\ \hline \end{array}$
17. $\begin{array}{r} 598 \\ +\ 59726 \\ \hline \end{array}$	18. $\begin{array}{r} 5793 \\ +\ 97642 \\ \hline \end{array}$	19. $\begin{array}{r} 98 \\ +\ 26497 \\ \hline \end{array}$	20. $\begin{array}{r} 8762 \\ +\ 86437 \\ \hline \end{array}$
21. $\begin{array}{r} 27596 \\ +\ 12385 \\ \hline \end{array}$	22. $\begin{array}{r} 96718 \\ +\ 5798 \\ \hline \end{array}$	23. $\begin{array}{r} 90738 \\ +\ 657 \\ \hline \end{array}$	24. $\begin{array}{r} 80064 \\ +\ 86 \\ \hline \end{array}$
25. $\begin{array}{r} 63574 \\ +\ 20049 \\ \hline \end{array}$	26. $\begin{array}{r} 10101 \\ +\ 99999 \\ \hline \end{array}$	27. $\begin{array}{r} 24500 \\ +\ 68809 \\ \hline \end{array}$	28. $\begin{array}{r} 65743 \\ +\ 856 \\ \hline \end{array}$
29. $\begin{array}{r} 24246 \\ +\ 24857 \\ \hline \end{array}$	30. $\begin{array}{r} 95357 \\ +\ 10041 \\ \hline \end{array}$	31. $\begin{array}{r} 16799 \\ +\ 30057 \\ \hline \end{array}$	32. $\begin{array}{r} 10978 \\ +\ 999 \\ \hline \end{array}$

Name: _____   Date: _____

Addition: *Addition Word Problems #1*

Directions: Write the addition problem for each situation and then solve.

1. Larry has been saving his money for two weeks. He started with $15. After the first week, he made an additional $24. At the end of the second week, he earned an additional $21.

   How much money does Larry have now? _____

2. Jane is the manager for her junior high football team. She must figure the statistics on rushing and receiving for her coach after each game. In this last game, John had 125 yards rushing and 115 yards receiving. Jack had 55 yards rushing and 77 yards receiving. James had 12 yards rushing and 53 yards receiving.

   How many total yards rushing were recorded? _____

   How many total yards were recorded for receiving? _____

   Total yards rushing and receiving? _____

3. Every year the State Department of Education needs to know how many computers are Internet-connected in each school. In Johnson Junior High, the library has 14 computers connected, 25 classrooms each contain one connected computer, the business room has 11 connected computers, and the office has five connected computers.

   How many total computers are connected to the Internet? _____

4. Jimmy's mother works in a veterinary clinic in town. She knows that there were six cats, seven dogs, and two rabbits in the clinic overnight. Today, the clinic accepted five cats and three rabbits. Tomorrow, she expects four more cats, six more dogs, and one more rabbit.

   How many cats, dogs, and rabbits will be in the clinic after tomorrow? _____

Name: _____ Date: _____

Addition: *Addition Word Problems #2*

Directions: Write the addition problem for each situation and then solve.

1. Kim is helping the school's librarian to count the number of fiction books in the library. She counted 37 books on the first bookshelf, 42 books on the second shelf, and 19 books on the third shelf.

    How many total fiction books are in the library?

    _____

2. Rosalie likes skateboarding. She estimates that on level surfaces she actually pushes four times for each block she is on. **If she skateboards for 10 blocks, how many pushes must she have done?**

    _____

3. Tim and his brother have been mowing lawns for money over the summer. Tim mowed three lawns, earning $5, $7, and $9, while his brother mowed four lawns, earning $6, $5, $8, and $10.

    How much money did Tim earn? _____

    His brother? _____

    Both together? _____

4. Sonny wants to total up how many hits he made during summer baseball games. He played 10 games over the summer. He made two hits in his first and fourth games. He made three hits in his second, fifth, seventh and ninth games. He made only one hit in his third and sixth games. Sonny made four hits in his eighth and tenth games.

    How many total hits did he make? _____

Name: _____ Date: _____

Addition: *Addition Word Problems #3*

Directions: Write the addition problem for each situation and then solve.

1. Jamie has compact discs of country, pop, and classical music. He has eight country CD's, 14 pop CD's, and seven classical CD's.

   How many total CD's does Jamie have?

   _____

2. Alex has a cookie and lemonade stand. He sells a glass of lemonade for 10 cents each and a cookie for 15 cents each. Today he sold six cookies and four glasses of lemonade.

   How much money in cents did Alex make from his stand? _____

3. Sun Yi enjoys golf. He plays nine holes and has the following strokes: 4, 5, 4, 3, 5, 5, 3, 6, and 4.

   How many strokes has Sun Yi played for these nine holes? _____

4. Ashlee has a stuffed animal collection. She has four rabbits, six bears, three dogs, five cats, and two raccoons.

   How many stuffed animals does Ashlee own? _____

5. To make money for a school dance, Serena's class sold cookies door to door. Three students sold 15 cookies each, four students sold 10 cookies each, and three students sold seven cookies each.

   How many cookies were sold? _____

Name: _____ Date: _____

Addition: *Addition Word Problems #4*

Directions: Write the addition problem for each situation and then solve.

1. Brent has a paper route. Every morning Brent delivers eight papers to Oak Street, 12 papers to Elm Street, seven papers to Spruce Street, and 11 papers to Maple Street.

    How many papers does Brent need to make all of his deliveries in the morning? _____

2. Washington has to ride the train to his grandparents' house. He must go through three stops and each stop is approximately 75 kilometers apart in distance.

    How far are his grandparents from his home? _____

3. In Wendy's school, there are three fourth-grade classes. In Mrs. Jones' class, there are 11 boys and eight girls. Mrs. Smith has nine boys and 12 girls. Miss Anderson has 10 boys and 10 girls.

    How many boys are in the fourth grade? _____

    Girls? _____

    How many students total? _____

4. Charlie plays basketball for his school. He made four three-point shots, 11 two-point shots, and five free throws for one point each during yesterday's game.

    How many points were made from three-point shots? _____

    Two-point shots? _____

    Free throws? _____

    How many total points did Charlie score in yesterday's game? _____

Name: _____ Date: _____

Addition: *Addition Word Problems #5*

Directions: Write the addition problem for each situation and then solve.

1. Linda is the pitcher for her softball team. She struck out six players in her first game, three players in her second game, five players in her third game, and seven players in her fourth game.

    How many players did Linda strike out? _____

2. Ivan has been saving his change for a week. He has saved three quarters, four dimes, and five nickels.

    How many cents in quarters did Ivan save? _____

    How many cents in dimes? _____

    How many cents in nickels? _____

    How much total in cents did he save? _____

3. Oscar is taking part in a reading program. He must count up the number of pages he has read in a month. Oscar read five books this month. One book had 115 pages, one had 140 pages, one had 209 pages, one had 157 pages, and one had 177 pages.

    How many total pages did Oscar read? _____

4. In Kathy's apartment building there are three different levels. The first level has 11 floors, the second level has nine floors, and the third level has seven floors.

    How many floors are in Kathy's building? _____

Subtraction: *Introduction*

As with addition, subtraction has two distinct types of subtraction. First is the **no renaming** or **no borrowing** problem where the student can easily take away the second number from the first. The second type is **renaming** or **borrowing** where the student must borrow from the number to the immediate left in the first number in order to take away the second number.

For the first type, use the table below. As with addition, find the first number in the top row and highlight the entire column. Then find the second number in the left column and highlight the entire row. Where the highlighted column and highlighted row meet is the difference.

Write 8 - 6 on the board. Use an overhead copy of the subtraction table from the back of the book and highlight the process listed above.

-	9	8	7	6	5	4	3	2	1	0
0	9	8	7	6	5	4	3	2	1	0
1	8	7	6	5	4	3	2	1	0	
2	7	6	5	4	3	2	1	0		
3	6	5	4	3	2	1	0			
4	5	4	3	2	1	0				
5	4	3	2	1	0					
6	3	2	1	0						
7	2	1	0							
8	1	0								
9	0									

The answer is 2.

Write 15 - 8 on the board. Use an overhead copy of the subtraction table from the back of the book and highlight the process listed above.

-	10	11	12	13	14	15	16	17	18
9	1	2	3	4	5	6	7	8	9
8	2	3	4	5	6	7	8	9	
7	3	4	5	6	7	8	9		
6	4	5	6	7	8	9			
5	5	6	7	8	9				
4	6	7	8	9					
3	7	8	9						
2	8	9							
1	9								

The answer is 7.

Have the students fill out the first and second subtraction practice sheets using the two tables.

Subtraction: *Introduction*

Write 25 - 8 on the board. Put the subtraction into a column form as below.

Example 1:

```
    25
-    8
```

How do you take 8 away from 5? You cannot do this. However, you can take 8 from 15. In order to turn 5 into 15, you must borrow 10 from 20.

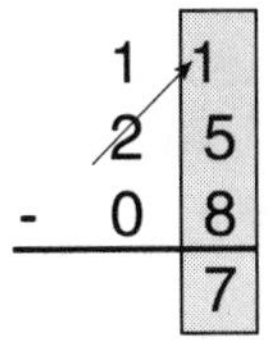

```
  1  1
  2  5
-  0  8
      7
```

Subtract 8 from 15 and you get 7. Now you have a 1 instead of a 2 above the 0 because you borrowed 10 to raise the 5 to 15.

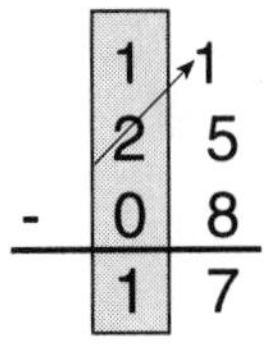

```
  1  1
  2  5
-  0  8
  1  7
```

Subtract 0 from 1 and you get 1. Therefore, the answer is 17.

There will be times when you must borrow more than once to solve a problem. Write 315 - 227 on the board. Show the borrowing of 10 from the 1 in 315 and then show the borrowing of 10 from the 3 in 315.

Example 2:

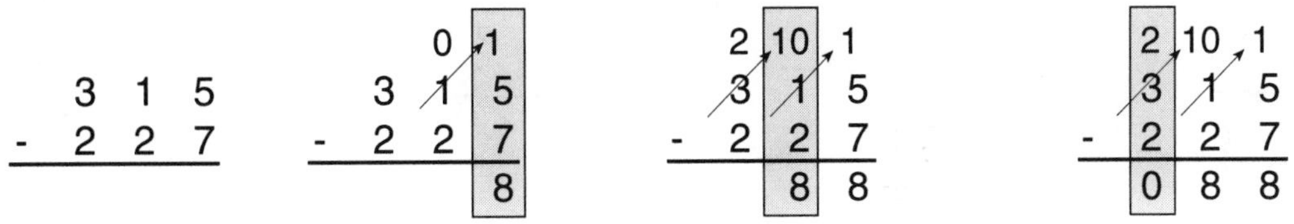

```
   3  1  5        0  1           2 10  1         2 10  1
-  2  2  7     3  1  5         3  1  5         3  1  5
             -  2  2  7      -  2  2  7      -  2  2  7
                      8           8  8         0  8  8
```

Name: _____ Date: _____

Subtraction: *Subtraction Practice #1*

Directions: Find the difference in each problem using the subtraction table.

1. 7 - 2 = 5

2. 9 - 0 = 9

3. 6 - 1 = 5

4. 8 - 7 = 1

5. 2 - 1 = 1

6. 1 - 1 = 0

7. 5 - 4 = 1

8. 4 - 1 = 3

9. 9 - 7 = 2

10. 7 - 4 = 3

11. 6 - 4 = 2

12. 8 - 3 = 5

13. 1 - 0 = 1

14. 0 - 0 = 0

15. 9 - 4 = 5

16. 9 - 3 = 6

17. 6 - 3 = 3

18. 7 - 5 = 2

19. 3 - 3 = 0

20. 5 - 2 = 3

21. 9 - 1 = 8

22. 8 - 5 = 3

23. 5 - 3 = 2

24. 6 - 2 = 4

25. 7 - 6 = 1

26. 8 - 2 = 6

27. 9 - 5 = 4

28. 7 - 7 = 0

29. 4 - 2 = 2

30. 9 - 8 = 1

Directions: Find the difference of each problem using the subtraction table.

1. 9
   - 5
   ___
    4

2. 8
   - 1
   ___
    7

3. 7
   - 2
   ___
    5

4. 3
   - 1
   ___
    2

5. 5
   - 0
   ___
    5

6. 4
   - 3
   ___
    1

7. 6
   - 4
   ___
    2

8. 2
   - 2
   ___
    0

9. 1
   - 0
   ___
    1

20

Name: _____   Date: _____

Subtraction: *Subtraction Practice #2*

Directions: Find the difference using the expanded subtraction table.

1.	18 - 9 = _____	2.	11 - 2 = _____
3.	17 - 9 = _____	4.	10 - 4 = _____
5.	16 - 8 = _____	6.	16 - 9 = _____
7.	15 - 9 = _____	8.	15 - 7 = _____
9.	14 - 7 = _____	10.	14 - 5 = _____
11.	13 - 6 = _____	12.	13 - 9 = _____
13.	12 - 3 = _____	14.	12 - 5 = _____
15.	11 - 4 = _____	16.	11 - 5 = _____
17.	10 - 9 = _____	18.	10 - 7 = _____
19.	17 - 8 = _____	20.	15 - 6 = _____
21.	16 - 7 = _____	22.	14 - 8 = _____
23.	15 - 8 = _____	24.	13 - 4 = _____
25.	14 - 6 = _____	26.	12 - 6 = _____
27.	13 - 5 = _____	28.	11 - 9 = _____
29.	12 - 8 = _____	30.	10 - 5 = _____

Directions: Find the difference using the expanded subtraction table.

1. $\begin{array}{r} 15 \\ -\ 6 \\ \hline \end{array}$	2. $\begin{array}{r} 17 \\ -\ 9 \\ \hline \end{array}$	3. $\begin{array}{r} 13 \\ -\ 8 \\ \hline \end{array}$
4. $\begin{array}{r} 11 \\ -\ 8 \\ \hline \end{array}$	5. $\begin{array}{r} 10 \\ -\ 7 \\ \hline \end{array}$	6. $\begin{array}{r} 16 \\ -\ 8 \\ \hline \end{array}$
7. $\begin{array}{r} 18 \\ -\ 9 \\ \hline \end{array}$	8. $\begin{array}{r} 14 \\ -\ 6 \\ \hline \end{array}$	9. $\begin{array}{r} 12 \\ -\ 7 \\ \hline \end{array}$

Name: _____ Date: _____

Subtraction: *Subtraction Practice #3*

Directions: Find the difference for each problem.

Example:

$$
\begin{array}{r} 25 \\ -\ \ 9 \\ \hline \end{array}
$$

$$
\begin{array}{r} 1\ \ \ \ \\ 2\!\!\!/\ 5 \\ -\ 0\ 9 \\ \hline 6 \end{array}
$$

$$
\begin{array}{r} 1\ \ 1 \\ 2\!\!\!/\ 5 \\ -\ 0\ 9 \\ \hline 1\ 6 \end{array}
$$

1. $\begin{array}{r} 56 \\ -\ 12 \\ \hline \end{array}$ 2. $\begin{array}{r} 97 \\ -\ 55 \\ \hline \end{array}$ 3. $\begin{array}{r} 32 \\ -\ 21 \\ \hline \end{array}$ 4. $\begin{array}{r} 94 \\ -\ 40 \\ \hline \end{array}$

5. $\begin{array}{r} 30 \\ -\ 10 \\ \hline \end{array}$ 6. $\begin{array}{r} 59 \\ -\ 34 \\ \hline \end{array}$ 7. $\begin{array}{r} 61 \\ -\ 20 \\ \hline \end{array}$ 8. $\begin{array}{r} 67 \\ -\ 36 \\ \hline \end{array}$

9. $\begin{array}{r} 94 \\ -\ 31 \\ \hline \end{array}$ 10. $\begin{array}{r} 56 \\ -\ 42 \\ \hline \end{array}$ 11. $\begin{array}{r} 28 \\ -\ 21 \\ \hline \end{array}$ 12. $\begin{array}{r} 25 \\ -\ 12 \\ \hline \end{array}$

13. $\begin{array}{r} 86 \\ -\ 61 \\ \hline \end{array}$ 14. $\begin{array}{r} 61 \\ -\ 30 \\ \hline \end{array}$ 15. $\begin{array}{r} 89 \\ -\ 29 \\ \hline \end{array}$ 16. $\begin{array}{r} 63 \\ -\ 61 \\ \hline \end{array}$

17. $\begin{array}{r} 96 \\ -\ 21 \\ \hline \end{array}$ 18. $\begin{array}{r} 99 \\ -\ 38 \\ \hline \end{array}$ 19. $\begin{array}{r} 97 \\ -\ 35 \\ \hline \end{array}$ 20. $\begin{array}{r} 91 \\ -\ 41 \\ \hline \end{array}$

21. $\begin{array}{r} 68 \\ -\ 25 \\ \hline \end{array}$ 22. $\begin{array}{r} 95 \\ -\ 15 \\ \hline \end{array}$ 23. $\begin{array}{r} 57 \\ -\ 46 \\ \hline \end{array}$ 24. $\begin{array}{r} 48 \\ -\ 25 \\ \hline \end{array}$

25. $\begin{array}{r} 37 \\ -\ 15 \\ \hline \end{array}$ 26. $\begin{array}{r} 29 \\ -\ 21 \\ \hline \end{array}$ 27. $\begin{array}{r} 92 \\ -\ 82 \\ \hline \end{array}$ 28. $\begin{array}{r} 77 \\ -\ 66 \\ \hline \end{array}$

29. $\begin{array}{r} 63 \\ -\ 32 \\ \hline \end{array}$ 30. $\begin{array}{r} 19 \\ -\ 10 \\ \hline \end{array}$ 31. $\begin{array}{r} 49 \\ -\ 21 \\ \hline \end{array}$ 32. $\begin{array}{r} 39 \\ -\ 37 \\ \hline \end{array}$

Name: _____ Date: _____

Subtraction: *Subtraction Practice #4*

Directions: Find the difference for each problem.

Example:

$$
\begin{array}{r} 3\ 1\ 5 \\ -\ 2\ 2\ 7 \\ \hline \end{array}
\qquad
\begin{array}{r} 0\ {}^{1} \\ 3\ \not{1}\ 5 \\ -\ 2\ 2\ 7 \\ \hline 8 \end{array}
\qquad
\begin{array}{r} 2\ 10\ {}^{1} \\ \not{3}\ \not{1}\ 5 \\ -\ 2\ 2\ 7 \\ \hline 8\ 8 \end{array}
\qquad
\begin{array}{r} 2\ 10\ {}^{1} \\ \not{3}\ \not{1}\ 5 \\ -\ 2\ 2\ 7 \\ \hline 0\ 8\ 8 \end{array}
$$

1.	211 - 85	2.	841 - 266	3.	730 - 125	4.	555 - 219
5.	912 - 134	6.	155 - 19	7.	203 - 116	8.	391 - 193
9.	617 - 421	10.	897 - 281	11.	641 - 118	12.	419 - 45
13.	719 - 209	14.	811 - 73	15.	986 - 911	16.	460 - 271
17.	318 - 105	18.	681 - 187	19.	510 - 57	20.	557 - 313
21.	711 - 99	22.	380 - 125	23.	477 - 101	24.	962 - 263
25.	819 - 225	26.	759 - 68	27.	700 - 368	28.	975 - 579
29.	864 - 468	30.	157 - 140	31.	842 - 139	32.	285 - 29

Name: _____   Date: _____

Subtraction: *Subtraction Practice #5*

Directions: Find the difference for each problem.

1. 9512 - 3899	2. 1294 - 1108	3. 6572 - 2963	4. 3286 - 1687
5. 9876 - 6810	6. 6789 - 3674	7. 6431 - 3496	8. 1346 - 1058
9. 4210 - 3500	10. 6497 - 2024	11. 6839 - 4921	12. 4995 - 3574
13. 9607 - 2907	14. 2869 - 684	15. 6779 - 3008	16. 5930 - 2148
17. 3397 - 2635	18. 9568 - 6847	19. 6859 - 5968	20. 7584 - 4857
21. 1937 - 958	22. 2973 - 1563	23. 3405 - 2589	24. 3007 - 2130
25. 9333 - 3779	26. 8644 - 1687	27. 2997 - 1963	28. 7893 - 3578
29. 1112 - 932	30. 3334 - 2341	31. 2555 - 1280	32. 8664 - 2941
33. 9176 - 3546	34. 7615 - 1599	35. 8246 - 6287	36. 6482 - 324

Name:_____ Date:_____

Subtraction: *Subtraction Practice #6*

Directions: Find the difference for each problem.

1. 38521 - 31050	2. 96210 - 25874	3. 32489 - 24863	4. 19873 - 12014
5. 94587 - 26871	6. 49375 - 35742	7. 58746 - 49875	8. 38695 - 10524
9. 78920 - 9841	10. 23234 - 6872	11. 55547 - 2541	12. 34109 - 24782
13. 45836 - 31005	14. 91573 - 49765	15. 57955 - 29873	16. 32106 - 25103
17. 23201 - 19523	18. 10287 - 9342	19. 19633 - 10056	20. 48627 - 35184
21. 27989 - 19635	22. 68829 - 37951	23. 97436 - 10256	24. 21986 - 3281
25. 99776 - 67010	26. 68754 - 35791	27. 26498 - 3867	28. 29701 - 2165
29. 11987 - 10095	30. 38999 - 35820	31. 67749 - 60102	32. 33333 - 24105
33. 65165 - 34930	34. 24994 - 21103	35. 95301 - 35799	36. 35975 - 23561

Name: _____ Date: _____

Subtraction: *Subtraction Word Problems #1*

Directions: Write the subtraction problem for each situation and then solve.

1. Ken has received his allowance of $20 for the month. He goes to a record store to buy some CD's of his favorite singer. One CD costs $5, one costs $7, and one costs $6.

   How much money will Ken have left after buying all three CD's?

   _____

2. Linda's beagle had seven puppies, and her black cat had nine kittens. She was able to give two puppies away to her friend Ashlee, three puppies to her friend Sam, and one puppy to her friend Stefanie. She was also able to give three kittens to her aunt Lucy, one kitten to her uncle Charlie, and three kittens to her cousin Brenda.

   How many puppies and kittens does Linda have left? _____

3. Brad has 120 minutes until he must be at the baseball game. He spends 15 minutes taking a shower, 10 minutes getting dressed, 20 minutes eating supper, and 30 minutes watching his favorite show.

   How many minutes before Brad has to be at the ball park? _____

4. Kelly is helping her father inventory his lumber yard. Kelly knows that her father started with 120 of the eight-foot 2 x 4's. Yesterday a contractor purchased 55 of the 2 x 4's and another customer purchased 20 of the 2 x 4's. Today the contractor returned and purchased another 25 of the 2 x 4's.

   How many 2 x 4's remain in the inventory? _____

Name: _____ Date: _____

Subtraction: *Subtraction Word Problems #2*

Directions: Write the subtraction problem for each situation and then solve.

1. Okito lives on 95th Street in his city. He often rides the bus to 73rd Street.

   How many blocks does he ride the bus each time he makes this trip? _____

2. Jill must read 1,000 pages this month to win her class's reading contest. She reads one book with 159 pages, one book with 230 pages, and two books with 300 pages each.

   How many pages must Jill read to win the contest?

   _____

3. Stefanie was visiting her father's office. He gave Stefanie a ream of paper containing 500 pages. Stefanie then made 120 copies of a letter, 105 copies of a newspaper article, and 157 copies of a note to the employees.

   How many pages are left in the ream of paper? _____

4. Ashlee was driving with her mother to Maine. Her mother told her that the total distance was 750 miles. Ashlee noticed that they drove 150 miles before stopping to eat lunch. She saw that they had gone another 350 miles before stopping for dinner.

   How many miles do Ashlee and her mother have left to drive? _____

Name: _____ Date: _____

Subtraction: *Subtraction Word Problems #3*

Directions: Write the subtraction problem for each situation and then solve.

1. Kathy is responsible for filling up the pencil dispenser. She filled the dispenser with 300 pencils. When she checked the dispenser on Monday, it had dispensed 15 pencils. On Tuesday it dispensed 30 pencils. On Wednesday it dispensed 56 pencils.

   How many pencils are left in the dispenser? _____

2. In a perfect baseball game, the home pitcher will pitch to 27 players. **If he strikes out 11 and causes 12 to ground out, how many players are left to face?**

   _____

3. Filicitie gets on the subway at 104th Street. She gets off at 93rd Street to shop. She then gets back on at 93rd Street and rides to 35th Street.

   How many blocks has Filicitie ridden the subway? _____

4. Quincy is placing tile on his bedroom floor. He has 144 tiles to be laid on the floor. After the first hour, Quincy had placed 28 tiles down. The second hour he placed 34 tiles. The third hour he placed 29 tiles.

   How many tiles are left after three hours? _____

Name: _____ Date: _____

Subtraction: *Subtraction Word Problems #4*

Directions: Write the subtraction problem for each situation and then solve.

1. Prince enjoys surfing. He began surfing this morning at 6:00 A.M. **If he finishes surfing at 11:45 A.M., how long has he surfed in hours and minutes?**

    _____

2. Tammy planted 450 beans in her garden. She counted 145 beans sprouting in the first row, 133 beans sprouting in the second row, and 149 beans sprouting in the third row.

    How many beans did not sprout? _____

3. Yolanda needs to check 750 lights in her Christmas display because the string does not light up. She checked 100 each hour for five hours.

    How many lights are left to be checked? _____

4. Mark works for a building contractor. He must keep track of how many of the 1,500 boards are used by each worker. Mark counted 166 boards used by Martino, 211 boards used by Lee, 321 boards used by Karen, and 319 boards used by Chen.

    How many boards are left at the end of the day? _____

5. A gallon of milk contains 128 ounces. One morning, three children drink an eight-ounce glass of milk, two children drink a six-ounce glass of milk, and one child drinks a 12-ounce glass of milk.

    How much milk is left? _____

Name: _____ Date: _____

Subtraction: *Subtraction Word Problems #5*

Directions: Write the subtraction problem for each situation and then solve.

1. Karen has 43 CD's in his collection. **If she lends 15 CD's to her friend John and 22 CD's to her brother Sam, how many CD's does Karen have left?**

    _____

2. The city dog pound has 20 dogs in its building. **If the pound is able to give away four dogs each day, how many dogs are left after five days?**

    _____

3. To pass the time Martika likes to time the trains that run by her house. The first train comes by around 5:30 A.M. and the last train comes by around 12:30 P.M.

    How many hours and minutes have passed between the first and last train?

    _____

4. Art wants to run 50 miles a week. He runs five miles on Monday, Wednesday, and Friday. He runs seven miles on Tuesday and Thursday. **If he runs 13 miles on Saturday, how many miles must Art run on Sunday to reach 50 miles?**

    _____

5. Mike has $30 for shopping. He buys two shirts for $8 each. He then buys three pairs of socks for $3 each.

    How much does Mike have left? _____

Multiplication: *Introduction*

Multiplication is a simplified form of addition. When we ask what 3 times 5 is, we are really asking, "If I add three groups of five together, what total will I have?" Look at the problem of 3 x 5.

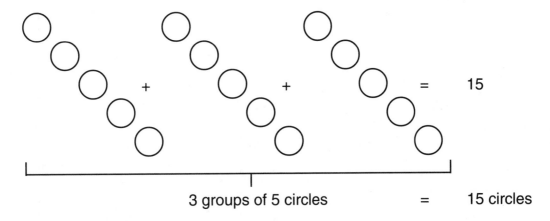

3 groups of 5 circles   =   15 circles

Another way to look at multiplication is using the numbers themselves. The multiplication problem 3 x 5, can be thought of as an addition problem of 5 + 5 + 5 = 10 + 5 = 15. However, this method can quickly become exhausting. For example, show 7 x 9 as an addition problem.

9 + 9 + 9 + 9 + 9 + 9 + 9 = 18 + 9 + 9 + 9 + 9 + 9 = 27 + 9 + 9 + 9 + 9 = 36 + 9 + 9 + 9 = 45 + 9 + 9 = 54 + 9 = 63

It is much easier if the students can learn basic multiplication, such as the 12 x 12 multiplication table provided in the back of this book. If you look at the multiplication table, you will see that as you move to the right, you are really just adding the number on the left one time for each space. If the process is repeated for each row, the multiplication table will be completely filled in. The students can fill in the blank table and keep it in their notebooks for future reference. The completed copy can be used to make a transparent copy for an overhead projector.

Multiplication: *Introduction*

To use the table for the example 7 x 9, find the 7 in the **top row** and highlight the **column**. Then find the 9 in the **first column** and highlight the **row**. Where the highlighted column and row meet is the answer: 63.

X	1	2	3	4	5	6	7	8	9	10	11	12
1	1	2	3	4	5	6	7	8	9	10	11	12
2	2	4	6	8	10	12	14	16	18	20	22	24
3	3	6	9	12	15	18	21	24	27	30	33	36
4	4	8	12	16	20	24	28	32	36	40	44	48
5	5	10	15	20	25	30	35	40	45	50	55	60
6	6	12	18	24	30	36	42	48	54	60	66	72
7	7	14	21	28	35	42	49	56	63	70	77	84
8	8	16	24	32	40	48	56	64	72	80	88	96
9	9	18	27	36	45	54	63	72	81	90	99	108
10	10	20	30	40	50	60	70	80	90	100	110	120
11	11	22	33	44	55	66	77	88	99	110	121	132
12	12	24	36	48	60	72	84	96	108	120	132	144

What about a problem like 15 x 5? This is not on the multiplication table, so how do we do this problem? To do this problem, we must understand that we multiply, then add.

First multiply the 5 and 5. From the table we know that this is 25. Like addition, we can only use the right number and must carry the 2 above the 1. Now we multiply the 5 and 1, which gives us 5. Next, add the 2 that we carried, and this gives an answer of 7.

```
              2            2
    15       1 5          1 5
  x  5     x   5        x   5
  -----    -----        -----
               5          7 5        The final answer is 75.
```

This process is repeated as needed until all multiplication is finished. Write 22 x 7 on the board. Show the multiplication process as given below.

```
              1            1
    22       2 2          2 2  ←——— factors
  x  7     x   7        x   7
  -----    -----        -----
               4         154  ←——— product
```

Multiplication: *Two Digits*

Multiplication of factors that are two digits or larger are handled similarly, except that each digit of the second factor is multiplied separately and then these individual products are added together to get the final product answer. Write 15 x 24 on the board.

The number 24 is 20 + 4. The first multiplication is the same as before with multiplying the 15 by the 4. The second multiplication involves multiplying the 15 by 20. However, only the 2 is used, and the multiplication begins under the second digit in the first product (under the 6 in 60). The empty space that is left under the 0 in 60 is filled in with a zero (0), and then the two products are added together.

```
                    2             1
     15            15            15            15
  x  24         x  24         x  24         x  24
  ------        ------        ------        ------
                   60            60            60
                                 30           300
                                             ------
                                              360
```

If students need more practice, work through the following examples with them.

Example 1:

```
     72            72            72            72
  x  30         x  30         x  30         x  30
  ------        ------        ------        ------
                   00            00            00
                                216           216
                                             ------
                                             2160
```

Example 2:

```
                   13            27
    629           629           629           629
  x  84         x  84         x  84         x  84
  ------        ------        ------        ------
                 2516          2516          2516
                 5032          5032          5032
                                            ------
                                            52836
```

Example 3:

```
                                 2
    413           413           413           413           413
  x 271         x 271         x 271         x 271         x 271
  ------        ------        ------        ------        ------
                  413           413           413           413
                               2891          2891          2891
                                              826           826
                                                           ------
                                                           111923
```

Name: _____ Date: _____

Multiplication: *Multiplication Practice #1*

Directions: Write each multiplication problem as an addition problem, then solve.

Example:

$3 \times 2 = 2 + 2 + 2 = 6$

$3 \times$ ⚽⚽ $= 6$ balls

⚽⚽ $+$ ⚽⚽ $+$ ⚽⚽ $= 6$ balls

1. 6×3 18

2. 7×5 35

3. 3×9 27

4. 2×10 20

5. 6×4 24

6. 4×12 48

7. 5×5 25

8. 1×11 11

9. 4×8 32

10. 12×2 24

11. 4×5 20

12. 6×6 36

13. 4×10 40

14. 9×3 27

15. 6×1 6

Name: _____ Date: _____

Multiplication: *Multiplication Practice #2*

Directions: Write the addition problems as multiplication problems, then solve.

1. 1 + 1 + 1 + 1 + 1 + 1 + 1 +1

    $8 \times 1 = 8$

2. 8 + 8 + 8 + 8 + 8 + 8

    $8 \times 6 = 48$

3. 7 + 7 + 7 + 7

    $4 \times 7 = 28$

4. 2 + 2 + 2 + 2

    $4 \times 2 = 8$

5. 12 + 12 + 12 + 12 + 12

    $5 \times 12 = 60$

6. 10 + 10 + 10 + 10 + 10 + 10

    $6 \times 10 = 60$

7. 6 + 6 + 6

    $3 \times 6 = 18$

8. 11 + 11 + 11 + 11+ 11

    $5 \times 11 = 55$

9. 9 + 9 + 9 + 9 + 9

    $9 \times 5 = 45$

10. 11 + 11 + 11

    $3 \times 11 = 33$

11. 4 + 4 + 4 + 4

    $4 \times 4 = 16$

12. 3 + 3 + 3 + 3 + 3 + 3

    $6 \times 3 = 18$

13. 5 + 5 + 5 + 5 + 5 + 5

    $5 \times 6 = 30$

14. 7 + 7 + 7 + 7 + 7 + 7 + 7

    $7 \times 7 = 49$

15. 3 + 3 + 3 + 3 + 3 + 3 + 3 + 3 + 3 + 3 + 3

    $3 \times 11 = 33$

35

Name: _____   Date: _____

Multiplication: *Multiplication Practice #3*

Directions: Multiply. Use the multiplication table.

1. 6
   x 7

2. 8
   x 2

3. 12
   x 5

4. 11
   x 12

5. 1
   x 3

6. 2
   x 5

7. 7
   x 4

8. 5
   x 9

9. 10
   x 6

10. 11
    x 8

11. 3
    x 12

12. 9
    x 7

13. 6
    x 3

14. 5
    x 12

15. 11
    x 10

16. 8
    x 8

17. 1
    x 8

18. 4
    x 6

19. 2
    x 9

20. 7
    x 6

21. 6
    x 10

22. 7
    x 2

23. 5
    x 5

24. 11
    x 11

25. 5
    x 7

26. 6
    x 6

27. 6
    x 8

28. 9
    x 3

29. 7
    x 7

30. 2
    x 7

31. 1
    x 1

32. 4
    x 4

33. 9
    x 9

34. 3
    x 2

35. 8
    x 2

36. 6
    x 5

Name: _____ Date: _____

Multiplication: *Multiplication Practice #4*

Directions: Multiply.

1. 17
    x 5

2. 25
    x 9

3. 36
    x 6

4. 19
    x 4

5. 12
    x 3

6. 44
    x 4

7. 51
    x 2

8. 63
    x 7

9. 75
    x 8

10. 82
     x 9

11. 95
     x 2

12. 21
     x 7

13. 41
     x 6

14. 66
     x 5

15. 53
     x 9

16. 39
     x 4

17. 23
     x 6

18. 45
     x 4

19. 15
     x 7

20. 69
     x 5

21. 56
     x 8

22. 35
     x 4

23. 27
     x 3

24. 46
     x 7

25. 74
     x 8

26. 61
     x 9

27. 86
     x 5

28. 38
     x 6

29. 18
     x 4

30. 42
     x 2

31. 37
     x 5

32. 68
     x 5

33. 58
     x 6

34. 28
     x 8

35. 76
     x 9

36. 16
     x 9

Name: _____   Date: _____

Multiplication: *Multiplication Practice #5*

Directions: Multiply. Show each multiplication step.

Example:

	2	1	
15	15	15	15
x 24	x 24	x 24	x 24
	60	60	60
		30	300
			360

1. 16
   x 35

2. 99
   x 16

3. 84
   x 43

4. 72
   x 51

5. 29
   x 88

6. 54
   x 78

7. 44
   x 57

8. 67
   x 94

9. 37
   x 24

10. 13
   x 18

11. 29
   x 28

12. 39
   x 39

13. 41
   x 21

14. 71
   x 30

15. 68
   x 57

16. 38
   x 85

17. 60
   x 11

18. 59
   x 15

19. 32
   x 32

20. 28
   x 29

Name: _____ Date: _____

Multiplication: *Multiplication Practice #6*

Directions: Multiply.

1. 127
    x   2

2. 257
    x   8

3. 645
    x   7

4. 279
    x   3

5. 167
    x   3

6. 498
    x   6

7. 455
    x   8

8. 287
    x   9

9. 962
    x   7

10. 853
     x   6

11. 743
     x   5

12. 199
     x   4

13. 210
     x   4

14. 333
     x   2

15. 348
     x   5

16. 781
     x   3

17. 987
     x   9

18. 456
     x   4

19. 226
     x   8

20. 645
     x   5

21. 317
     x   9

22. 784
     x   8

23. 618
     x   6

24. 733
     x   7

25. 555
     x   8

26. 574
     x   5

27. 488
     x   6

28. 884
     x   3

29. 399
     x   3

30. 686
     x   6

31. 717
     x   4

32. 813
     x   2

33. 221
     x   3

34. 300
     x   8

35. 607
     x   9

36. 905
     x   7

Name: _____   Date: _____

Multiplication: *Multiplication Practice #7*

Directions: Multiply. Show each multiplication step.

1. 357
    x   25

2. 951
    x   24

3. 735
    x   62

4. 195
    x   75

5. 852
    x   13

6. 396
    x   57

7. 963
    x   44

8. 258
    x   78

9. 714
    x   97

10. 174
     x   86

11. 349
     x   75

12. 493
     x   64

13. 946
     x   24

14. 649
     x   19

15. 806
     x   27

16. 680
     x   64

17. 779
     x   33

18. 343
     x   34

19. 618
     x   48

20. 857
     x   46

21. 559
     x   37

22. 927
     x   58

23. 784
     x   69

24. 956
     x   52

Name: _____   Date: _____

Multiplication: *Multiplication Practice #8*

Directions: Multiply.

1. 1264 x 3	2. 2456 x 7	3. 5741 x 8	4. 4987 x 9
5. 2874 x 6	6. 1086 x 7	7. 9571 x 4	8. 3482 x 6
9. 1667 x 5	10. 8588 x 2	11. 7281 x 7	12. 3479 x 8
13. 1397 x 9	14. 2486 x 5	15. 3416 x 3	16. 9746 x 7
17. 5465 x 6	18. 9876 x 7	19. 5206 x 9	20. 6347 x 5
21. 4725 x 6	22. 3997 x 4	23. 8426 x 8	24. 6842 x 2
25. 1784 x 3	26. 2665 x 4	27. 6551 x 8	28. 5783 x 5
29. 9634 x 9	30. 9782 x 8	31. 9389 x 7	32. 9469 x 9
33. 8876 x 4	34. 8451 x 6	35. 8968 x 7	36. 8327 x 8

Name: _____   Date: _____

Multiplication: *Multiplication Practice #9*

Directions: Multiply. Show each multiplication step.

1. 5524 x 97	2. 6057 x 62	3. 8991 x 46	4. 3425 x 31
5. 5103 x 92	6. 6741 x 83	7. 4167 x 79	8. 9467 x 64
9. 2583 x 61	10. 5832 x 42	11. 8352 x 72	12. 3852 x 81
13. 3971 x 91	14. 9713 x 62	15. 7139 x 84	16. 1397 x 95
17. 6793 x 63	18. 8623 x 52	19. 3046 x 85	20. 8709 x 74
21. 2240 x 32	22. 5566 x 54	23. 8844 x 87	24. 9993 x 65

Name: _____ Date: _____

Multiplication: *Multiplication Practice #10*

Directions: Multiply. Show each multiplication step.

1. 3571 x 351	2. 3684 x 842	3. 9382 x 963	4. 8293 x 741
5. 9087 x 208	6. 7590 x 980	7. 6871 x 873	8. 3187 x 542
9. 5715 x 558	10. 9784 x 974	11. 7617 x 341	12. 3047 x 465
13. 5317 x 152	14. 7852 x 248	15. 1679 x 675	16. 9647 x 863
17. 9628 x 807	18. 8271 x 706	19. 4521 x 643	20. 2462 x 157

Name: _____   Date: _____

Multiplication: *Multiplication Word Problems #1*

Directions: Write the multiplication problem for each situation and then solve.

1. Fred recycles aluminum cans. He gets 30 cents per pound of aluminum. **If Fred has 17 pounds of aluminum cans, how much money in cents will Fred get?**

    _____

2. Ingrid's father drives a bus for the city. Her father's bus can hold 62 passengers at one time. He estimates that his bus is filled at least seven times a day.

    How many passengers has Ingrid's father had on his bus in one day? _____

3. Bob reads 11 books with 120 pages each.

    How many pages does Bob read? _____

4. Steve's truck holds 20 gallons of gas. **If Steve fills up his truck 52 times a year, how many gallons of gas does Steve purchase in a year?**

    _____

5. The school's bleachers have seven sections. Each section can seat 55 people.

    How many total people can sit in the bleachers? _____

Name: _____ Date: _____

Multiplication: *Multiplication Word Problems #2*

Directions: Write the multiplication problem for each situation and then solve.

1. Sherry saves her money. She plans to save $5 per week for a full year. **If there are 52 weeks in a year, how much money will Sherry save?**

   _____

2. Tom's garden has eight tomato plants. **If each plant produces 137 tomatoes, how many tomatoes are produced in the garden?**

   _____

3. Melissa notices that her bus has 22 seats. **If each seat is capable of seating three students, how many students can her bus carry?**

   _____

4. Paul is running a lemonade stand. He sells a glass of lemonade for 25 cents each. Today he sold 25 glasses of lemonade.

   How much money did Paul earn today, in cents? _____

5. There are 24 balloons in a box. **If Penny's class buys 18 boxes for the carnival, how many balloons does her class have?**

   _____

Name: _____ Date: _____

Multiplication: *Multiplication Word Problems #3*

Directions: Write the multiplication problem for each situation and then solve.

1. Jerry and his brother picked up walnuts last fall. They filled nine bags with 375 nuts per bag.

   How many walnuts did Jerry and his brother pick up?

   _____

2. Alexia has been skateboarding for three hours. She estimates that she can skateboard around 24 blocks in an hour.

   How many blocks has Alexia skated around? _____

3. A ton of rock weighs 2,000 pounds. **If Greg's dad buys 13 tons of rock, how much does this weigh in pounds?**

   _____

4. Vern estimates that it takes about eight gallons of water to wash one load of clothes. **If he washes 315 loads of clothes in one year, how many gallons of water are used?**

   _____

5. Velma is an avid golfer. On her recent 14-day vacation, she played 18 holes on six different courses and 27 holes on three courses.

   How many total holes were played on the 18-hole courses? _____

   How many total holes were played on the 27-hole courses? _____

Name: _____ Date: _____

Multiplication: *Multiplication Word Problems #4*

Directions: Write the multiplication problem for each situation and then solve.

1. The librarian thinks that each shelf should contain around 47 books. **If there are 114 shelves in the library, how many books should there be?**

    _____

2. Eugene plays basketball. He made 3 three-point shots, 11 two-point shots, and 9 free throws for one point each.

    Total how many points he made from three-point shots. _____

    From two-point shots? _____

    From free throws? _____

3. In football, a touchdown is worth six points. A field goal is three points. A team scores seven touchdowns and four field goals.

    How many points were from touchdowns? _____

    How many points were from field goals? _____

4. School lunch and breakfast cost $2 per day total. **If a student is at school for 175 days, how much money is spent on lunch and breakfast combined?**

    _____

5. **If a gallon of water is 128 ounces, how many ounces are in 128 gallons?**

    _____

Name: _____ Date: _____

Multiplication: *Multiplication Word Problems #5*

Directions: Write the multiplication problem for each situation and then solve.

1. Amy is helping with her science class's fund raiser. They are selling beanbag toy mascots for $5.00 each. The class received five boxes with 144 in each box.

   How many beanbag toy mascots does the class have to sell? _____

   How much money will the class bring in if they sell all of the beanbag toys? _____

2. Jack's school is hosting a basketball tournament. There are eight schools attending the tournament and each school will be bringing 12 players.

   How many players total will be at the tournament? _____

3. Ronda rides the subway for 25 minutes in the morning and 31 minutes in the afternoon. She rides the subway six days a week.

   How many minutes a week does she ride in the morning? _____

   How many minutes a week does she ride in the afternoon? _____

4. Tim has been saving his money. He has 50 dimes, 44 nickels, 125 pennies, and 20 quarters saved.

   How many cents does he have in dimes? _____

   Nickels? _____

   Pennies? _____

   Quarters? _____

   How much does he have saved total? _____

Division: *Introduction*

Division is simply a form of subtraction. When we write 12 ÷ 4 we are really asking, "How many 4's are in 12?" We do the subtraction 12 -④= 8 -④= 4 -④= 0. The answer is 3 because we were able to subtract three 4's from 12.

Another method is to use the multiplication table in reverse. In the case of 15 ÷ 3, find the 15 in the 3 column. Now follow this row to the left and you will find the number 5. Therefore there are five 3's in 15.

X	1	2	③	4	5	6	7	8	9	10	11	12
1	1	2	3	4	5	6	7	8	9	10	11	12
2	2	4	6	8	10	12	14	16	18	20	22	24
3	3	6	9	12	15	18	21	24	27	30	33	36
4	4	8	12	16	20	24	28	32	36	40	44	48
⑤	←5	10	⑮	20	25	30	35	40	45	50	55	60
6	6	12	18	24	30	36	42	48	54	60	66	72
7	7	14	21	28	35	42	49	56	63	70	77	84
8	8	16	24	32	40	48	56	64	72	80	88	96
9	9	18	27	36	45	54	63	72	81	90	99	108
10	10	20	30	40	50	60	70	80	90	100	110	120
11	11	22	33	44	55	66	77	88	99	110	121	132
12	12	24	36	48	60	72	84	96	108	120	132	144

Again the same problem using subtraction is 15 -③= 12 -③= 9 -③= 6 -③= 3 -③= 0. You can see there are five 3's in 15.

When the final answer after subtraction is zero, we say there is "no remainder." However, if we would have had a number left that was less than the number we were subtracting, we say that it is the "remainder," and we show it with a capital R after the number. Write 17 ÷ 4 on the board. Work it as a subtraction problem. 17 -④= 13 -④= 9 - ④= 5 -④= 1. We have four 4's but a remainder of 1. The answer is 4 R1.

Long division is the same process as subtraction, except we do not show each subtraction step. Instead we show the answer (or quotient) above the dividend, and the divisor to the left of the dividend. Write the problem 5)15 on the board.

$$
\begin{array}{r}
3 \quad \longleftarrow \text{ quotient} \\
\text{divisor} \longrightarrow 5\overline{)15} \quad \longleftarrow \text{ dividend} \\
\underline{15} \quad \longleftarrow \text{ this is the multiplication of 3 and 5, then subtract} \\
0 \quad \longleftarrow \text{ there is no remainder}
\end{array}
$$

Division: *Introduction*

Write 8)26 on the board. Have the students find the number in the 8 column of the multiplication table that is closest to or equal to 26 without being greater than 26. They should find 24. Have them look left in the row with 24, and the quotient will be 3. This means that the long division would look like this:

$$\begin{array}{r} 3 \\ 8\overline{)26} \\ \underline{24} \\ 2 \end{array}$$

This time after subtraction we are left with a number less than the divisor. This is our remainder. The answer is written as 3 R2.

All division occurs from left to right, one digit at a time. We must first check to see if the divisor is larger or smaller than the first digit of the dividend. If it is larger than the first digit (8 is larger than the 2 in 26), then we must compare the divisor with the first and second digit together (8 compared to 26). If the divisor is smaller, we do the division and start the quotient above the second digit. If it is larger, we keep adding digits until we can divide.

Write 5)65 on the board. Compare the divisor 5 with the first digit, 6, of 65. The number 5 is smaller than the 6, therefore we start the division here. How many 5's are in 6? One. The number 1 will go above the 6. The multiplication of 5 and 1 is 5 and this goes below the 6. Now subtract 5 from 6 and you get 1. This will not be the remainder because we still have another digit in 65 to consider—the digit is the number 5. Bring the number 5 down and now instead of 1 we have 15. How many 5's are in 15? Three. The number 3 gets written next to the 1 in the quotient. Multiply 5 and 3 and you get 15. Write this under the 15 and subtract. The remainder is zero. The answer is 13.

$$5\overline{)65} \qquad \begin{array}{r} 1 \\ 5\overline{)65} \\ \underline{5} \\ 1 \end{array} \qquad \begin{array}{r} 1 \\ 5\overline{)65} \\ \underline{5\downarrow} \\ 15 \end{array} \qquad \begin{array}{r} 13 \\ 5\overline{)65} \\ \underline{5} \\ 15 \\ \underline{15} \\ 0 \end{array}$$

Division: *Introduction*

Another way to perform division is to not allow any remainders. Instead the division continues until the remainder is equal to zero. To do this we must go into the decimal places. Write the problem 8$)$26 on the board again. This time have the students do the division, but stop at the remainder of 2. Now we do not want to have a remainder, so we place a decimal point to the right of the quotient 3 and the dividend 26. We add a couple of zeros to the right of the dividend 26. Now bring the first zero down next to the 2. We have 20. How many 8's are in 20? Two. The number 2 goes to the right of the decimal point in the quotient. Eight times 2 is 16. Subtract this from 20. Now we have a remainder of 4. Drop down the next zero and ask how many 8's are in 40. Five. The number 5 goes next to the 2 in the quotient. Multiply the 8 and 5 and then subtract. Now the remainder is zero and we can stop.

$$
\begin{array}{r} 3 \\ 8\,\overline{)26} \\ \underline{24} \\ 2 \end{array}
\qquad
\begin{array}{r} 3 \\ 8\,\overline{)26} \\ \underline{24} \\ 2 \end{array}
\qquad
\begin{array}{r} 3. \\ 8\,\overline{)26.00} \\ \underline{24} \\ 2 \end{array}
\qquad
\begin{array}{r} 3. \\ 8\,\overline{)26.00} \\ \underline{24}\downarrow \\ 20 \end{array}
\qquad
\begin{array}{r} 3.2 \\ 8\,\overline{)26.00} \\ \underline{24} \\ 20 \\ \underline{16} \\ 4 \end{array}
\qquad
\begin{array}{r} 3.25 \\ 8\,\overline{)26.00} \\ \underline{24} \\ 20 \\ \underline{16}\downarrow \\ 40 \\ \underline{40} \\ 0 \end{array}
$$

Sometimes the quotient will have a zero in the middle. Write 6$)$1218 on the board. After you do the first division of 12 by 6, you get a subtraction of zero. This does not mean that the problem is finished, because we still have to do the 18 portion of 1218. Instead we drop down the 1 and ask how many 6's are in 1? Zero. The number 0 will be written to the right of the 2 in the quotient. Now drop down the 8 and ask how many 6's are in 18? Three. The number 3 is written to the right of the 20 in the quotient and there is no remainder. Since there is no part of the dividend that still needs to be taken care of, the problem is finished and the quotient is 203.

$$
6\,\overline{)1218}
\qquad
\begin{array}{r} 2 \\ 6\,\overline{)1218} \\ \underline{12} \\ 0 \end{array}
\qquad
\begin{array}{r} 20 \\ 6\,\overline{)1218} \\ \underline{12}\downarrow \\ 01 \end{array}
\qquad
\begin{array}{r} 203 \\ 6\,\overline{)1218} \\ \underline{12}\downarrow \\ 018 \\ \underline{18} \\ 0 \end{array}
$$

Name: _____ Date: _____

Division: *Division Practice #1*

Directions: Write each division problem as a subtraction problem, then solve. There may be remainders.

Example:		
$9 \div 3$	$9 - 3 = 6 - 3 = 3 - 3 = 0$	3 R0

1. $10 \div 3$

2. $12 \div 5$

3. $8 \div 3$

4. $17 \div 6$

5. $12 \div 4$

6. $16 \div 7$

7. $18 \div 6$

8. $5 \div 2$

9. $4 \div 1$

10. $9 \div 4$

11. $10 \div 2$

12. $11 \div 6$

13. $15 \div 5$

14. $19 \div 7$

15. $17 \div 8$

16. $19 \div 5$

17. $12 \div 6$

18. $14 \div 4$

Name: _____ Date: _____

Division: *Division Practice #2*

Directions: Write the subtraction problem as a division problem, then solve. There may be remainders.

Example: $10 - 2 = 8 - 2 = 6 - 2 = 4 - 2 = 2 - 2 = 0$

$$2\overline{)10} \\ \underline{10} \\ 0$$

with quotient 5

1. $19 - 8 = 11 - 8 = 3$

2. $15 - 4 = 11 - 4 = 7 - 4 = 3$

3. $8 - 5 = 3$

4. $17 - 5 = 12 - 5 = 7 - 5 = 2$

5. $16 - 9 = 7$

6. $14 - 3 = 11 - 3 = 8 - 3 = 5 - 3 = 2$

7. $18 - 6 = 12 - 6 = 6 - 6 = 0$

8. $9 - 3 = 6 - 3 = 3 - 3 = 0$

9. $12 - 5 = 7 - 5 = 2$

10. $13 - 4 = 9 - 4 = 5 - 4 = 1$

11. $7 - 2 = 5 - 2 = 3 - 2 = 1$

12. $19 - 6 = 13 - 6 = 7 - 6 = 1$

Name: _____ Date: _____

Division: *Division Practice #3*

Directions: Divide. Use the multiplication table.

1. $5\overline{)5}$ 1

2. $2\overline{)8}$ 4

3. $3\overline{)6}$ 2

4. $2\overline{)2}$ 1

5. $1\overline{)6}$ 6

6. $4\overline{)8}$ 2

7. $1\overline{)7}$ 7

8. $7\overline{)7}$ 1

9. $2\overline{)6}$ 3

10. $1\overline{)8}$ 8

11. $3\overline{)9}$ 3

12. $2\overline{)0}$ 0

13. $3\overline{)15}$ 5

14. $9\overline{)18}$ 2

15. $10\overline{)90}$ 9

Name: _____ Date: _____

Division: *Division Practice #4*

Directions: Divide. Write answers in remainder form.

Example:

$$6\overline{)14}$$ gives 2, 12, remainder 2 → 2 R2

---

1. $2\overline{)9}$

2. $3\overline{)8}$

3. $4\overline{)6}$

4. $2\overline{)5}$

5. $5\overline{)9}$

6. $2\overline{)7}$

7. $5\overline{)8}$

8. $7\overline{)9}$

9. $5\overline{)6}$

10. $2\overline{)3}$

11. $3\overline{)4}$

12. $3\overline{)5}$

13. $10\overline{)44}$

14. $8\overline{)25}$

15. $3\overline{)16}$

Name: _____ Date: _____

Division: *Division Practice #5*

Directions: Divide. Write answers in decimal form. Use the multiplication table.

Example:
$$
\begin{array}{r}
1.25 \\
4\overline{)5.00} \\
\underline{4} \\
10 \\
\underline{8} \\
20 \\
\underline{20} \\
0
\end{array}
$$

1. $2\overline{)3}$

2. $5\overline{)9}$

3. $5\overline{)6}$

4. $4\overline{)9}$

5. $2\overline{)5}$

6. $4\overline{)6}$

7. $2\overline{)7}$

8. $5\overline{)8}$

9. $2\overline{)9}$

10. $4\overline{)7}$

11. $6\overline{)9}$

12. $5\overline{)7}$

Name: _____ Date: _____

Division: *Division Practice #6*

Directions: Divide. Write answers in remainder form if required.

1. $5\overline{)19}$ 2. $2\overline{)22}$ 3. $5\overline{)41}$

4. $6\overline{)63}$ 5. $6\overline{)71}$ 6. $8\overline{)51}$

7. $6\overline{)18}$ 8. $8\overline{)29}$ 9. $9\overline{)35}$

10. $4\overline{)46}$ 11. $3\overline{)52}$ 12. $4\overline{)64}$

13. $8\overline{)82}$ 14. $8\overline{)95}$ 15. $9\overline{)76}$

Name: _____ Date: _____

Division: *Division Practice #7*

Directions: Divide. Write answers in decimal form if required.

1. $5\overline{)31}$

2. $5\overline{)42}$

3. $6\overline{)57}$

4. $6\overline{)75}$

5. $9\overline{)63}$

6. $5\overline{)32}$

7. $6\overline{)54}$

8. $5\overline{)61}$

9. $8\overline{)60}$

10. $5\overline{)41}$

11. $5\overline{)65}$

12. $6\overline{)69}$

13. $8\overline{)98}$

14. $4\overline{)37}$

15. $8\overline{)64}$

Name: _____ Date: _____

Division: *Division Practice #8*

Directions: Divide. Write answers in remainder form if required.

1. $21\overline{)96}$

2. $25\overline{)85}$

3. $17\overline{)63}$

4. $11\overline{)24}$

5. $15\overline{)65}$

6. $19\overline{)79}$

7. $12\overline{)48}$

8. $18\overline{)64}$

9. $33\overline{)97}$

10. $31\overline{)86}$

11. $24\overline{)72}$

12. $17\overline{)66}$

13. $24\overline{)59}$

14. $15\overline{)36}$

15. $16\overline{)80}$

Name: _____ Date: _____

Division: *Division Practice #9*

Directions: Divide. Write answers in decimal form if required.

1. 15)‾96‾

2. 10)‾63‾

3. 24)‾78‾

4. 18)‾81‾

5. 12)‾90‾

6. 18)‾99‾

7. 17)‾68‾

8. 15)‾93‾

9. 31)‾93‾

10. 12)‾75‾

11. 29)‾87‾

12. 16)‾84‾

13. 25)‾80‾

14. 16)‾34‾

15. 24)‾75‾

Name: _____ Date: _____

Division: *Division Practice #10*

Directions: Divide. Write answers in remainder form if required.

1. $6\overline{)125}$

2. $8\overline{)492}$

3. $7\overline{)612}$

4. $9\overline{)830}$

5. $3\overline{)186}$

6. $9\overline{)294}$

7. $5\overline{)525}$

8. $6\overline{)810}$

9. $7\overline{)372}$

10. $8\overline{)729}$

11. $7\overline{)265}$

12. $4\overline{)408}$

13. $3\overline{)921}$

14. $2\overline{)831}$

15. $4\overline{)619}$

Name: _____ Date: _____

Division: *Division Practice #11*

Directions: Divide. Write answers in decimal form if required.

1. $5\overline{)126}$

2. $6\overline{)573}$

3. $5\overline{)142}$

4. $8\overline{)138}$

5. $4\overline{)832}$

6. $8\overline{)556}$

7. $4\overline{)293}$

8. $5\overline{)317}$

9. $9\overline{)243}$

10. $9\overline{)945}$

11. $6\overline{)567}$

12. $2\overline{)873}$

13. $4\overline{)101}$

14. $7\overline{)875}$

15. $8\overline{)225}$

Name: _____ Date: _____

Division: *Division Practice #12*

Directions: Divide. Write answers in remainder form if required.

1. $26 \overline{)690}$ 2. $45 \overline{)966}$ 3. $50 \overline{)758}$

4. $31 \overline{)631}$ 5. $61 \overline{)549}$ 6. $33 \overline{)770}$

7. $94 \overline{)990}$ 8. $75 \overline{)999}$ 9. $81 \overline{)900}$

10. $73 \overline{)438}$ 11. $15 \overline{)232}$ 12. $27 \overline{)967}$

13. $65 \overline{)395}$ 14. $19 \overline{)390}$ 15. $44 \overline{)264}$

Name: _____ Date: _____

Division: *Division Practice #13*

Directions: Divide. Write answers in decimal form if required.

1. $24 \overline{)318}$ 2. $30 \overline{)615}$ 3. $62 \overline{)930}$

4. $15 \overline{)243}$ 5. $16 \overline{)156}$ 6. $28 \overline{)483}$

7. $21 \overline{)756}$ 8. $36 \overline{)234}$ 9. $76 \overline{)665}$

10. $72 \overline{)846}$ 11. $14 \overline{)406}$ 12. $48 \overline{)732}$

13. $48 \overline{)294}$ 14. $80 \overline{)684}$ 15. $56 \overline{)511}$

Name: _____ Date: _____

Division: *Division Practice #14*

Directions: Divide. Write answers in remainder form if required.

1. $9 \overline{)3213}$ 2. $7 \overline{)3402}$ 3. $6 \overline{)3915}$

4. $5 \overline{)1477}$ 5. $8 \overline{)3287}$ 6. $4 \overline{)1501}$

7. $7 \overline{)1550}$ 8. $9 \overline{)1412}$ 9. $6 \overline{)1486}$

10. $4 \overline{)3409}$ 11. $7 \overline{)3934}$ 12. $3 \overline{)1357}$

13. $9 \overline{)2115}$ 14. $5 \overline{)1274}$ 15. $7 \overline{)2252}$

Name: _____ Date: _____

Division: *Division Practice #15*

Directions: Divide. Write answers in decimal form if required.

1. $7\overline{)6734}$ 2. $5\overline{)1436}$ 3. $4\overline{)1633}$

4. $6\overline{)4431}$ 5. $9\overline{)4626}$ 6. $8\overline{)1964}$

7. $5\overline{)3127}$ 8. $4\overline{)3254}$ 9. $3\overline{)1551}$

10. $6\overline{)2325}$ 11. $5\overline{)2096}$ 12. $8\overline{)4898}$

13. $9\overline{)2916}$ 14. $7\overline{)1582}$ 15. $8\overline{)6005}$

Name: _____ Date: _____

Division: *Division Practice #16*

Directions: Divide. Write answers in remainder form if required.

1. $77 \overline{)3858}$ 2. $45 \overline{)1495}$ 3. $86 \overline{)5504}$

4. $83 \overline{)1418}$ 5. $29 \overline{)1028}$ 6. $38 \overline{)1243}$

7. $95 \overline{)2280}$ 8. $85 \overline{)2650}$ 9. $62 \overline{)1521}$

10. $69 \overline{)4506}$ 11. $73 \overline{)1145}$ 12. $41 \overline{)2571}$

13. $22 \overline{)2761}$ 14. $55 \overline{)1416}$ 15. $17 \overline{)1622}$

Name: _____ Date: _____

Division: *Division Practice #17*

Directions: Divide. Write answers in decimal form if required.

1. $96\overline{)2160}$ 2. $68\overline{)1105}$ 3. $92\overline{)5842}$

4. $24\overline{)1950}$ 5. $30\overline{)2172}$ 6. $55\overline{)4741}$

7. $34\overline{)3230}$ 8. $26\overline{)3159}$ 9. $25\overline{)7955}$

10. $36\overline{)3105}$ 11. $41\overline{)5207}$ 12. $82\overline{)7503}$

13. $22\overline{)8382}$ 14. $18\overline{)2925}$ 15. $32\overline{)2820}$

Name: _____ Date: _____

Division: *Division Practice #18*

Directions: Divide. Write answers in remainder form if required.

1. $214 \overline{)4287}$

2. $125 \overline{)2875}$

3. $308 \overline{)8016}$

4. $197 \overline{)6124}$

5. $327 \overline{)4920}$

6. $254 \overline{)6350}$

7. $318 \overline{)6996}$

8. $149 \overline{)4774}$

9. $186 \overline{)3373}$

10. $241 \overline{)5323}$

11. $162 \overline{)5684}$

12. $229 \overline{)9629}$

Name: _____ Date: _____

Division: *Division Practice #19*

Directions: Divide. Write answers in decimal form if required.

1. $362 \overline{)9593}$

2. $308 \overline{)9625}$

3. $220 \overline{)3861}$

4. $235 \overline{)9729}$

5. $124 \overline{)7750}$

6. $244 \overline{)4697}$

7. $104 \overline{)8658}$

8. $102 \overline{)7395}$

9. $148 \overline{)8769}$

10. $216 \overline{)9531}$

11. $128 \overline{)7184}$

12. $108 \overline{)7695}$

Name: _____ Date: _____

Division: *Division Word Problems #1*

Directions: Write the division problem for each situation and then solve.

1. Three students work mowing lawns all summer. The students make $150 total.

   How much will each student receive if each gets the same amount?

   _____

2. A school has 175 students in it. There are seven grades in the school and each grade has the same number of students in it.

   How many students are in each grade? _____

3. A class of 25 students equally collected $2350 in a fund raiser.

   How much did each student raise? _____

4. A building is 150 feet high, and each floor is ten feet high.

   How many floors are in the building? _____

5. Ling and her brother are planning to drive to Alaska. It is 1500 miles to Alaska from their home. **If each hour of driving they are able to go 50 miles, how many hours will it take to get to Alaska?**

   _____

Name: _____ Date: _____

Division: *Division Word Problems #2*

Directions: Write the division problem for each situation and solve. Use remainders if necessary.

1. A store donated a box containing 365 cookies to a school fund-raising committee. **If the students wrap the cookies eight in a package, how many packages will there be?**

    _____

2. Bill and his seven friends deliver papers in the morning. **If the paper truck drops off 1045 papers, how many does each delivery person get?**

    _____

3. A computer's hard drive is 640,000,000 bytes in size. **If each kilobyte is 1024 bytes, how many kilobytes are in the computer's hard drive?**

    _____

4. A gas truck delivers 10,000 gallons of gas to a gas station. **If the station has six tanks, how many gallons will go into each tank?**

    _____

5. James estimates that he walks at least 258 blocks each week. **If he walks six days a week, how many blocks will he walk each day?**

    _____

Name: _____ Date: _____

Division: *Division Word Problems #3*

Directions: Write the division problem for each situation and solve. Use the decimal form if necessary.

1. Oliver has saved $456.25 over the past year. **If there are 365 days in a year, how much did Oliver save each day?**

   _____

2. Over the course of a season, the football team scored 356 points. **If the team played ten games, how many points were scored in each game?**

   _____

3. Nancy earned $26.25 from recycling aluminum cans. **If she had 75 pounds of cans, how much did she get for each pound?**

   _____

4. At the basketball game last night, the ticket takers made $475. They estimated that 125 people attended the game.

   How much did each person pay? _____

5. Jackie always goes surfing on Saturdays and Sundays. **If there are four weekends this month and she plans to surf a total of 56 hours, how many hours per day is this?**

   _____

Name: _____ Date: _____

Division: *Division Word Problems #4*

Directions: Write the division problem for each situation and solve. Use the decimal form if necessary.

1. Alyssa has $37.50 to spend. **If she buys 32 milk shakes for her class, how much does each milk shake cost?**

   _____

2. **If a gallon is 128 ounces, how many 8-ounce glasses can be filled from a gallon?**

   _____

3. Tom rushed for 1260 yards in the nine games he played this season in football.

   How many yards did he average in each game? _____

4. Luigi is conducting a survey of how many people use the subway at 98th Street each hour. He found that 264 people used the subway each hour. He counted 1,056 people during the time he was there.

   How many hours did Luigi conduct his survey? _____

5. A mountain top is 17,688 feet high. **If there are 5280 feet in a mile, how many miles high is the mountain top?**

   _____

Name: _____   Date: _____

Division: *Division Word Problems #5*

Directions: Write the division problem for each situation and solve. Use the decimal form if necessary.

1. Rita's class has 24 students in it. The class weighed each student and totaled the weight. The total weight was 2544 pounds.

    How much does each student weigh? _____

2. Angela ran 725 miles this year. **If she ran 200 days, how many miles did she run each day?**

    _____

3. Ashton found $20 in the street. He wants to divide it evenly between himself and his three friends.

    How much will each get? _____

4. Juan played golf over the weekend. He played at the local 18-hole golf course. **If his final total number of strokes was 90, how many strokes per hole did he average?**

    _____

5. A doctor's office has 300 milliliters of vaccine for the flu available. **If each shot contains 4 milliliters of the vaccine, how many patients can the doctor's office help?**

    _____

Order of Operations: *Introduction*

Sometimes it is necessary to add, subtract, multiply, and/or divide in the same problem. When this must be done, it must be done in a specific way. **Order of operations** in math means that all groupings within brackets, braces, or parentheses must be done first. After all groupings have been completed, the next step is to work out all multiplication and division. The final step is to do all addition and subtraction. Complete all operations from left to right in the proper order.

For example, write $2 + 3 \times 4$ on the board. Now ask the students to find the answer. Ask how many students figured 20 to be the answer and how many figured 14 to be the answer. Fourteen is the correct answer. The multiplication must be done before the addition, as shown below.

$$2 + 3 \times 4 = 2 + 12 = 14$$

Now write this problem on the board. $(2 + 3) \times 4$. According to the order of operations, the grouping within the parentheses must be done first. So the sum of 2 and 3 is figured, and then it is multiplied by 4 to give an answer of 20.

Write the following problem on the board. Have the students find the answer.

$$[9 - (5 + 2) + 3] \times 4 \div 2$$

In this problem, students should work on the operations in the brackets before the multiplication and division.

The operation in parentheses should be done first.

$$(5 + 2) = 7$$

Next, students should complete the subtraction and addition in the brackets from left to right.

$$[9 - 7 + 3] = 5$$

Finally, students should complete the multiplication and division from left to right.

$$5 \times 4 \div 2 = 20 \div 2 = 10$$

Name: _____ Date: _____

Order of Operations: *Practice #1*

Directions: Find the answer using order of operations. Show each step.

1. $4 + 3 \times 6 = 22$
   $4 + 18 = 22$

2. $5 - 1 \times 2 = 3$
   $5 - 2 = 3$

3. $24 - 8 + 4 = 20$
   $16 + 4 = 20$

4. $12 \div 4 + 7 = 10$
   $3 + 7 = 10$

5. $9 \times 2 - 8 = 10$
   $18 - 8 = 10$

6. $16 \div 2 + 4 = 12$
   $8 + 4 = 12$

7. $12 - 6 \div 2 = 9$
   $12 - 3 = 9$

8. $15 - 6 \div 3 = 13$
   $15 - 2 = 13$

9. $16 + 9 \times 2 = 34$
   $16 + 18 = 34$

10. $8 \times 3 - 12 = 12$
    $24 - 12 = 12$

11. $18 \div 3 + 4 = 10$
    $6 + 4 = 10$

12. $6 \times 4 + 4 = 28$
    $24 + 4 = 28$

13. $8 - 8 \div 4 = 6$
    $8 - 2 = 6$

14. $2 + 9 \div 3 = 5$
    $2 + 3 = 5$

15. $16 - 12 \div 2 = 10$
    $16 - 6 = 10$

Name: _____ Date: _____

Order of Operations: *Practice #2*

Directions: Find the answer using order of operations. Show each step.

1. $(2 + 1) \times (3 + 1) = 12$
   $3 \times 4 = 12$

2. $(8 - 5) \div (6 - 2)$
   $3 \div 4 = \frac{3}{4}$

3. $(12 + 1) \times (3 - 2) = 13$
   $13 \times 1 = 13$

4. $(12 \div 4) + (15 \div 3) = 8$
   $3 + 5 = 8$

5. $(4 \times 2) - (18 \div 6) = 5$
   $8 - 3 = 5$

6. $(16 \div 4) + (12 - 4) = 12$
   $4 + 8 = 12$

7. $(16 - 2) \div (10 - 3) = 2$
   $14 \div 7 = 2$

8. $(8 + 2) \times (12 - 6) = 60$
   $10 \times 6 = 60$

9. $(3 + 5) \div (5 - 3) = 4$
   $8 \div 2 = 4$

10. $(12 \div 2) - (4 \times 1) = 2$
    $6 - 4 = 2$

11. $(20 \div 5) + (8 \times 2) = 20$
    $4 + 16 = 20$

12. $(18 \div 3) - (12 \div 4) = 3$
    $6 - 3 = 3$

13. $(8 - 6) \times (9 + 2) = 22$
    $2 \times 11 = 22$

14. $(16 + 2) \div (12 - 4) = 2 R2$
    $18 \div 8 = 2 R2$

15. $(25 - 12) + (18 \div 3) = 7$
    $13 + 6 = 7$

$8\overline{)18}$

Name: _____ Date: _____

Order of Operations: *Assorted Word Problems #1*

Directions: Find the answers using addition, subtraction, multiplication, and division.

1. Spencer, Hunter, and Conner pooled their money and then split it so each had the same amount. Spencer had $25, Hunter had $23, and Conner had $24.

   How much would each have after they split up the total equally?

   _____

2. January and March had eight inches of rain each month. July and August had six inches of rain each month. **If the remaining eight months had one inch each month, what is the total rainfall for the year?**

   _____

3. Jim bought three shirts at $10 each. He then purchased five shorts at $8 each.

   How much did Jim spend on clothes? _____

4. Herb has two cases of pencils and an additional three packs that each contain six pencils. **If a case holds 24 pencils, how many pencils does Herb have?**

   _____

5. Megan saved up $4 a day for 25 days. She then bought three CD's for $15 each.

   How much money does Megan have left? _____

Name: _____ Date: _____

Order of Operations: *Assorted Word Problems #2*

Directions: Find the answers using addition, subtraction, multiplication, and division.

1. A gallon contains 128 ounces and a half-gallon contains 64 ounces. Wendy's mother bought three gallons of punch and six half-gallons of juice

   How many total ounces of beverages did Wendy's mother buy?

   _____

2. Becky has $700 in her checking account. She buys two jackets for $45 each and three pairs of shoes for $25 each. She then saves up $125.

   How much money does Becky have? _____

3. April and Lexi have driven seven hours a day for six days. They slept five nights for eight hours each night. They spent another two hours a day for six days eating at different restaurants. They spent seven hours each day for six days sightseeing.

   How many total hours have they been gone? _____

4. Dale plays basketball. He scored five three-point baskets, 13 two-point baskets, and 11 free throws at one point each.

   How many points total did Dale score? _____

5. Andy is a runningback for his school's football team. In the first three games, Andy rushed for 125 yards in each game and caught passes for 85 yards in each game.

   How many yards total did Andy rush and receive in his first three games?

   _____

Fractions: *Introduction*

Fractions are just numbers that show how much of an item is still present. Look at the diagram below.

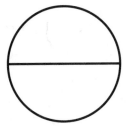  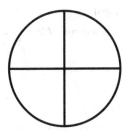

The first circle has two parts, so each part is one-half of the whole. The second circle has three parts, so each part is one-third of the whole. The third circle has four parts, so each part is one-fourth of the whole. This continues for as many parts as can be displayed.

A fraction is made up of two parts, the numerator or the top number, and the denominator or the bottom number. The **numerator** tells how many parts are present. The **denominator** tells how many parts the whole is broken into.

$$\text{denominator} \rightarrow \frac{3}{4} \leftarrow \text{numerator}$$

For the fraction three-fourths, the denominator 4 tells you how many parts the circle is broken into. The circle has four equal slices. The numerator 3 tells you that we are using only three of the four slices.

A whole circle of four equal slices with all four parts being used is the following fraction: $\frac{4}{4}$.

Whenever you have the same numerator and denominator, the fraction is equal to the number 1. So four-fourths equal 1, three-thirds equal 1, and two-halves equal 1.

$$\frac{4}{4} = 1 \qquad \frac{3}{3} = 1 \qquad \frac{2}{2} = 1$$

Ch 8

Fractions: *Introduction*

Fractions can be added and subtracted as well. To add or subtract a fraction, the denominator must be the same number. If the denominators are the same, then all you do is add or subtract the numerators. The answer is the addition or subtraction of the numerators written over the denominator.

$$\frac{1}{5} + \frac{2}{5} = \frac{1+2}{5} = \frac{3}{5}$$

same denominators   add the numerators

The same method is used for subtraction. First make sure the denominators are the same, then subtract the numerators, then write the difference above the denominator.

$$\frac{3}{7} - \frac{1}{7} = \frac{3-1}{7} = \frac{2}{7}$$

If students need more practice, work the following problems with them.

Example 1:

$$\frac{7}{16} + \frac{8}{16} = \frac{7+8}{16} = \frac{15}{16}$$

Example 2:

$$\frac{3}{9} + \frac{4}{9} = \frac{3+4}{9} = \frac{7}{9}$$

Example 3:

$$\frac{8}{16} - \frac{7}{16} = \frac{8-7}{16} = \frac{1}{16}$$

Example 4:

$$\frac{6}{8} - \frac{3}{8} = \frac{6-3}{8} = \frac{3}{8}$$

Name: _____ Date: _____

Fractions: *Fractions Practice #1*

Directions: For each problem, break the circle into the number of parts represented by the number.

1. 4

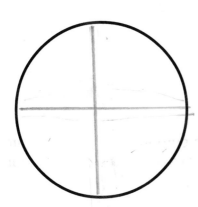

2. 3

3. 5

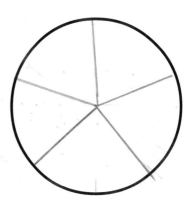

4. 7

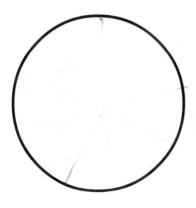

5. 6

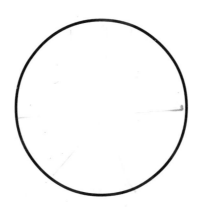

6. 10

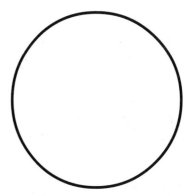

7. 12

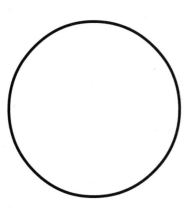

8. 9

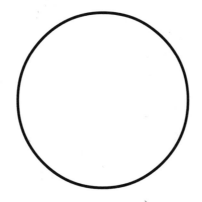

9. 15

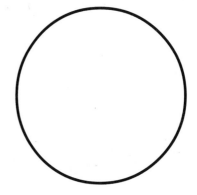

Name: _____ Date: _____

Fractions: *Fractions Practice #2*

Directions: Add or subtract each fraction.

1. $\dfrac{1}{8} + \dfrac{3}{8} = \dfrac{4}{8}$

2. $\dfrac{4}{5} + \dfrac{1}{5} = \dfrac{5}{5}$

3. $\dfrac{5}{9} + \dfrac{2}{9} = \dfrac{7}{9}$

4. $\dfrac{7}{8} - \dfrac{3}{8} = \dfrac{4}{8}$

5. $\dfrac{3}{4} - \dfrac{1}{4} = \dfrac{2}{4}$

6. $\dfrac{3}{5} + \dfrac{2}{5} = \dfrac{5}{5}$

7. $\dfrac{12}{13} - \dfrac{3}{13} = \dfrac{9}{13}$

8. $\dfrac{4}{7} + \dfrac{2}{7} = \dfrac{6}{7}$

9. $\dfrac{1}{5} + \dfrac{1}{5} = \dfrac{2}{5}$

10. $\dfrac{4}{9} - \dfrac{2}{9} = \dfrac{2}{9}$

11. $\dfrac{8}{11} + \dfrac{1}{11} = \dfrac{9}{10}$

12. $\dfrac{9}{14} - \dfrac{3}{14} = \dfrac{6}{14}$

13. $\dfrac{15}{16} - \dfrac{11}{16} = \dfrac{4}{16}$

14. $\dfrac{2}{4} + \dfrac{2}{4} = \dfrac{4}{4}$

15. $\dfrac{5}{12} - \dfrac{2}{12} = \dfrac{3}{12}$

16. $\dfrac{6}{10} + \dfrac{3}{10} = \dfrac{9}{10}$

17. $\dfrac{4}{15} + \dfrac{10}{15} = \dfrac{14}{15}$

18. $\dfrac{1}{2} + \dfrac{1}{2} = 1$

19. $\dfrac{18}{20} - \dfrac{13}{20} = \dfrac{5}{20}$

20. $\dfrac{3}{3} - \dfrac{2}{3} = \dfrac{1}{3}$

Name: _____ Date: _____

Fractions: *Fractions Practice #3*

Directions: Add or subtract each fraction.

1. $\frac{2}{8} + \frac{3}{8} =$ 5/8

2. $\frac{4}{7} - \frac{3}{7} =$ 1/7

3. $\frac{8}{11} + \frac{2}{11} =$ 10/11

4. $\frac{11}{12} - \frac{6}{12} =$ 5/12

5. $\frac{12}{19} - \frac{3}{19} =$ 9/19

6. $\frac{6}{18} + \frac{8}{18} =$ 14/18

7. $\frac{15}{17} - \frac{4}{17} =$ 11/17

8. $\frac{4}{9} + \frac{4}{9} =$ 8/18

9. $\frac{1}{8} + \frac{6}{8} =$ 7/8

10. $\frac{6}{12} - \frac{2}{12} =$ 4/12

11. $\frac{8}{14} + \frac{3}{14} =$ 11/14

12. $\frac{15}{15} - \frac{5}{15} =$ 10/15

13. $\frac{8}{8} - \frac{6}{8} =$ 2/8

14. $\frac{10}{16} + \frac{4}{16} =$ 14/16

15. $\frac{10}{16} - \frac{4}{16} =$ 6/16

16. $\frac{1}{5} + \frac{3}{5} =$ 4/5

17. $\frac{7}{20} + \frac{4}{20} =$ 11/20

18. $\frac{3}{10} + \frac{7}{10} =$ 10/10

19. $\frac{8}{14} - \frac{7}{14} =$ 1/14

20. $\frac{4}{4} - \frac{2}{4} =$ 2/4

Name: _____ Date: _____

Fractions: *Fractions Practice #4*

Directions: Determine the equivalent fraction by first drawing the fraction as parts of a circle based on the number in the denominator. Then color in the number of parts represented by the numerator. Finally determine what new fraction is completed. The first problem is completed for you.

1. $\frac{3}{6}$ = $\frac{1}{2}$

2. $\frac{2}{8}$ = $\frac{1}{4}$

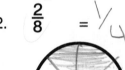

3. $\frac{2}{4}$ = $\frac{1}{2}$

4. $\frac{4}{8}$ = $\frac{1}{2}$

5. $\frac{2}{10}$ = $\frac{1}{5}$

6. $\frac{2}{6}$ = $\frac{1}{3}$

7. $\frac{3}{9}$ = $\frac{1}{3}$

8. $\frac{5}{10}$ = $\frac{1}{2}$

9. $\frac{6}{9}$ = $\frac{2}{3}$

10. $\frac{3}{12}$ = $\frac{1}{4}$

Geometry: *Triangles Introduction*

Triangles are objects with three sides that meet in three **vertices** or corners. Draw the four three-sided objects shown below on the board. Point out that the first two objects are not triangles because they do not have two of their sides meeting at a vertex or corner. The third and fourth objects are triangles because all three sides meet at vertices.

1.   2.   3.   4.

Triangles are classified or identified by the measure of the angles at the vertices and by the length of each side. If all three angles measure less than 90°, the triangle is called an **acute triangle**. If one of the three angles measures more than 90°, it is called an **obtuse triangle**. If one of the three angles is exactly 90°, it is called a **right triangle**. If all three sides have different lengths, it is called a **scalene triangle**. If at least two sides have exactly the same length, it is called an **isosceles triangle**. If all three sides are the same length, the triangle is called an **equilateral triangle**. By the way, if all three sides of a triangle have the same length, all three angles are the same measure: 60°.

Draw the following examples on the board.

Acute triangle   **Obtuse triangle**   **Right triangle**

Scalene triangle   **Isosceles triangle**   **Equilateral triangle**

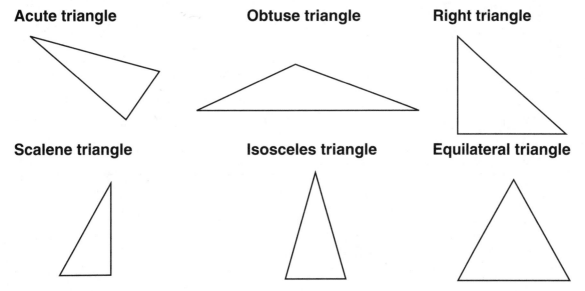

Triangles can be classified using either the angle measures or the side lengths. For example, the following three triangles are all scalene, but the first is acute, the second is obtuse, and the third is right.

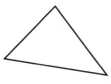
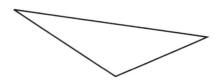
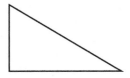

Name: _____ Date: _____

Geometry: *Triangles Practice #1*

Directions: Classify each triangle by its angles and side lengths.

1. _____

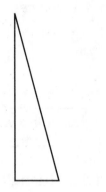

2. _____

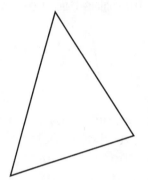

3. _____

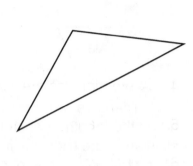

4. _____

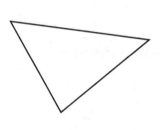

5. _____

6. _____

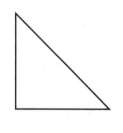

7. _____

8. _____

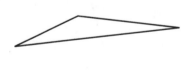

9. _____

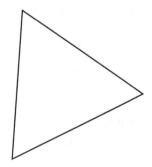

Name: _____   Date: _____

Geometry: *Triangles Practice #2*

Directions: Answer the following as sometimes, always, or never.

1. Acute triangles are right triangles.   _____

2. Acute triangles are obtuse triangles.   _____

3. Acute triangles are scalene triangles.   _____

4. Acute triangles are isosceles triangles.   _____

5. Acute triangles are equilateral triangles.   _____

6. Equilateral triangles are scalene triangles.   _____

7. Equilateral triangles are isosceles triangles.   _____

8. Equilateral triangles are acute triangles.   _____

9. Equilateral triangles are obtuse triangles.   _____

10. Equilateral triangles are right triangles.   _____

11. Obtuse triangles are right triangles.   _____

12. Obtuse triangles are acute triangles.   _____

13. Obtuse triangles are scalene triangles.   _____

14. Obtuse triangles are equilateral triangles.   _____

15. Obtuse triangles are isosceles triangles.   _____

16. Isosceles triangles are scalene triangles.   _____

17. Isosceles triangles are obtuse triangles.   _____

18. Isosceles triangles are equilateral triangles.   _____

19. Isosceles triangles are acute triangles.   _____

20. Isosceles triangles are right triangles.   _____

Name: _____ Date: _____

Geometry: *Triangles Practice #2 (Continued)*

Directions: Answer the following as sometimes, always, or never.

21. Right triangles are scalene triangles.   _____

22. Right triangles are acute triangles.   _____

23. Right triangles are obtuse triangles.   _____

24. Right triangles are isosceles triangles.   _____

25. Right triangles are equilateral triangles.   _____

26. Scalene triangles are acute triangles.   _____

27. Scalene triangles are obtuse triangles.   _____

28. Scalene triangles are right triangles.   _____

29. Scalene triangles are isosceles triangles.   _____

30. Scalene triangles are equilateral triangles.   _____

Directions: Answer the following questions.

1. Why are equilateral triangles always acute triangles? _____

   _____

2. Why are acute triangles never right triangles? _____

   _____

3. Why are equilateral triangles always isosceles triangles? _____

   _____

   _____

4. Why are scalene triangles never isosceles triangles? _____

   _____

   _____

Geometry: *Quadrilaterals Introduction*

Quadrilaterals are four-sided objects that have all sides meeting at four **vertices** or corners. Draw the four-sided objects below on the board. Show how the first two objects are quadrilaterals because all four sides meet at four vertices or corners. Point out how the last two objects are not quadrilaterals because the four sides do not meet at four vertices.

1. 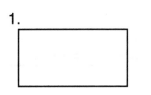 2. 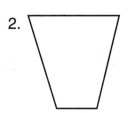 3. 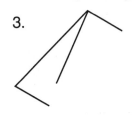 4.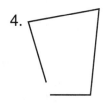

Quadrilaterals are classified or identified by the lengths of their sides and the measure of the angles (just as triangles were). However, with quadrilaterals you must also consider whether the opposite sides are parallel or not.

If a four-sided object does not have any parallel opposite sides, it is called simply a **quadrilateral**.

Quadrilateral - no parallel sides.

If a four-sided object has only one pair of parallel opposite sides, it is called a **trapezoid**.

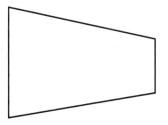

Trapezoid - only one pair of parallel sides.

If a four-sided object has both pairs of opposite sides parallel, it is called a **parallelogram**.

Parallelogram - both pairs of sides parallel

　　　91

Geometry: *Quadrilaterals Introduction*

Now that we have dealt with the notion of parallel sides to classify four-sided objects, we must now consider the idea of measures of angles. For this we only consider parallelograms. If a parallelogram has angles that measure 90° each, it is called a **rectangle**.

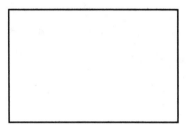

Rectangle - parallelogram with 90° angles

If you consider a parallelogram with all four sides of equal length, we call that a **rhombus**.

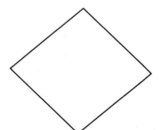

Rhombus - parallelogram with four equal sides.

Now if you have a parallelogram with four 90° angles and four sides of equal length, we call that a **square**.

Square - parallelogram with 90° angles and four equal sides

Name: _____ Date: _____

Geometry: *Quadrilaterals Practice #1*

Directions: Match the term with the correct shape. Answers may be used more than once.

____ 1. Quadrilateral   A.   B.   C.

____ 2. Trapezoid

____ 3. Parallelogram

____ 4. Rectangle   D.    E.   F.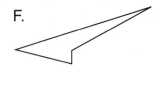

____ 5. Rhombus

____ 6. Square

Directions: Fill in the missing classifications using the following terms: **Square**, **Rhombus**, **Rectangle**, **Parallelogram**, and **Trapezoid**.

Quadrilateral

One pair of sides parallel   Both pairs of sides parallel

_____   _____

Four 90° angles   Four equal sides

_____   _____

Four equal sides and 90° angles

_____

Key:

Arrows pointing down mean sometimes.

Arrows pointing up mean always.

93

Name: _____ Date: _____

Geometry: *Quadrilaterals Practice #2*

Directions: Use the quadrilateral diagram below to answer the questions as always, sometimes, or never.

Key:

Arrows pointing down mean sometimes.

Arrows pointing up mean always.

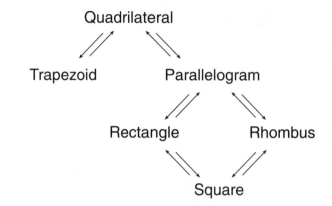

1. A trapezoid is always, sometimes, or never a parallelogram. _____

2. A trapezoid is always, sometimes, or never a square. _____

3. A quadrilateral is always, sometimes, or never a rectangle. _____

4. A quadrilateral is always, sometimes, or never a rhombus. _____

5. A square is always, sometimes, or never a rectangle. _____

6. A square is always, sometimes, or never a parallelogram. _____

7. A parallelogram is always, sometimes, or never a quadrilateral. _____

8. A parallelogram is always, sometimes, or never a rhombus. _____

9. A rectangle is always, sometimes, or never a quadrilateral. _____

10. A rectangle is always, sometimes, or never a trapezoid. _____

11. A rhombus is always, sometimes, or never a square. _____

12. A rhombus is always, sometimes, or never a parallelogram. _____

13. A trapezoid is always, sometimes, or never a rhombus. _____

14. A quadrilateral is always, sometimes, or never a trapezoid. _____

15. A square is always, sometimes, or never a trapezoid. _____

16. A parallelogram is always, sometimes, or never a square. _____

17. A rectangle is always, sometimes, or never a parallelogram. _____

18. A rhombus is always, sometimes, or never a trapezoid. _____

19. A square is always, sometimes, or never a quadrilateral. _____

20. A quadrilateral is always, sometimes, or never a square. _____

Geometry: *Three-Dimensional Figures Introduction*

Three-dimensional figures are important for students' understanding of their environment. From these figures come a student's understanding of volume, surface area, and common shapes. In this lesson we will deal only with the common shapes and leave the volume and surface area for the next year.

For us, we need only consider three types of three-dimensional shapes. The first is a pyramid, which should be recognized by most students. The second is a prism. The third is the circular objects.

Pyramids are three-dimensional figures with triangles for sides or faces. We classify pyramids based on what shape the base is, not the sides. Look at the triangular pyramid below. Note the reference to the face, the edge, a vertex, and the base. The dashed lines represent edges that are on the back side of the pyramid.

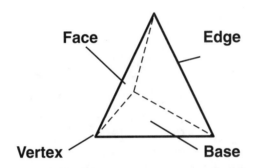

You can have any type of pyramid by simply changing the base. Below you can see a rectangular pyramid, a pentagonal pyramid (pyramid with a five-sided base), and a hexagonal pyramid (pyramid with a six-sided base).

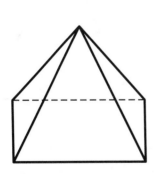

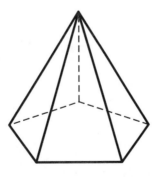

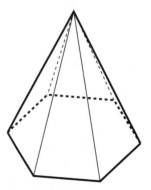

Rectangular pyramid   **Pentagonal Pyramid**   **Hexagonal Pyramid**

Geometry: *Three-Dimensional Figures Introduction*

The **prism** differs from the pyramid in that the sides or faces are rectangles instead of triangles. The prism still gets its name from the shape of the base. Below are the triangular prism, rectangular prism, and pentagonal prism.

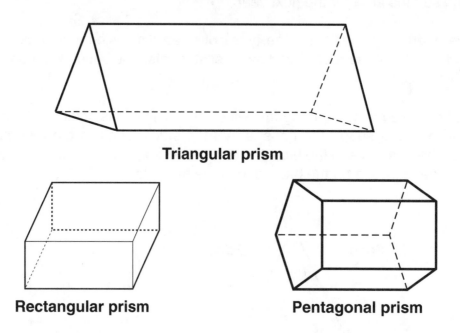

Triangular prism

Rectangular prism   **Pentagonal prism**

The final type of three-dimensional figure is the **circular objects**. There are three distinct shapes for circular objects. The **cone** closely resembles a pyramid except it has a circular base. The **cylinder** closely resembles a prism except it has circular bases as well. The **sphere** is a true three-dimensional circle. All three are shown below.

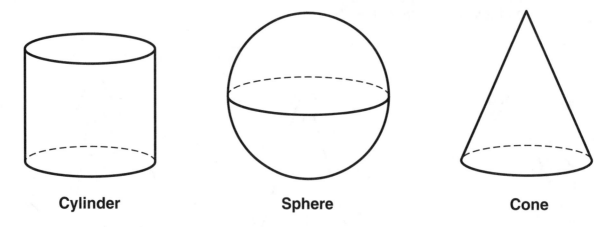

Cylinder   **Sphere**   **Cone**

At this time it is only important that the students can properly identify the differences between the various shapes.

Name: _____ Date: _____

Geometry: *Three-Dimensional Figures Practice #1*

Directions: Match the terms with the correct figures.

A.
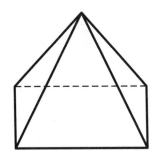

B.
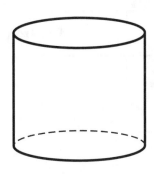

C.
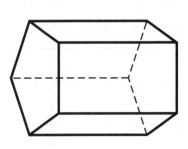

D.
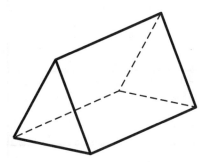

E.
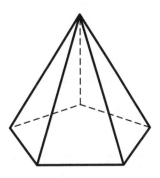

F.
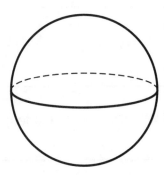

G.
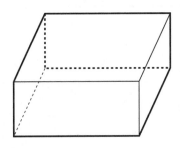

H.
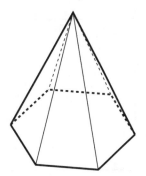

I.

___ 1. Triangular prism   ___ 2. Cone   ___ 3. Rectangular prism

___ 4. Rectangular pyramid   ___ 5. Cylinder   ___ 6. Pentagonal pyramid

___ 7. Pentagonal prism   ___ 8. Sphere   ___ 9. Hexagonal pyramid

97

Name: _____ Date: _____

Geometry: *Three-Dimensional Figures Practice #2*

Directions: Write out the names of the various shapes given the name of the bases.

Base Shape	Pyramid	Prism
1. Octagon (8 sides)		
2. Decagon (10 sides)		
3. Heptagon (7 sides)		
4. Nonagon (9 sides)		
5. Dodecagon (12 sides)		
6. Icosagon (20 sides)		
7. Undecagon (11 sides)		

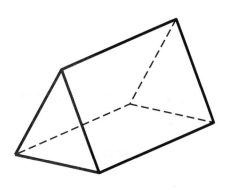 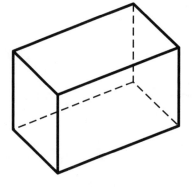 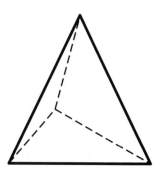

Metrics: *Introduction*

Metrics is simply another tool for measurement of length, area, volume, and temperature. It is simpler to use since it relies on the same principle that the place value system utilizes. Look at the diagram below and notice how it matches up with the place value system.

The place value diagram looks like this:

If the place value diagram is modified, it can easily show the metric prefixes as follows:

It is easy to see from these comparisons that **kilo** means 1000, **hecto** means 100, **deca** means 10, **deci** means one-tenth, **centi** means one-hundredth, and **milli** means one-thousandth.

Also, the basic units for the metric system are **meter** for measuring length, **gram** for measuring weight, and **liter** for measuring volume or capacity. This means that a kiloliter is 1000 liters, because kilo means 1000.

Metric symbols will have two parts at most. The **stem** will consist of the actual unit name for the type of measurement used. The **prefix** will come before the stem, if it is used, and will describe how large the unit actually is.

Let's look at the stem or the unit for each type of measurement:

Type of Measurement	Unit Name	Symbol
Length	meter	m
Mass/weight	gram	g
Volume/capacity	liter	L or l

6-6 p. 216
6-9 p. 222

Metrics: *Introduction*

The prefixes describe the size of the measurement and are listed below from largest to smallest (all possible prefixes are not listed).

Prefix Name	Symbol	Decimal value	Fraction value	Description
kilo	k	1,000		thousand
hecto	h	100		hundred
deca or deka	da	10		ten
deci	d	0.1	1/10	tenth
centi	c	0.01	1/100	hundredth
milli	m	0.001	1/1000	thousandth

By placing the prefix name with the stem, you get the full description of the measurement. For example:

Prefix		Stem		Full name		Description		Decimal Description		Equivalent Symbol
centi	+	meter	=	centimeter	=	a hundredth of a meter	=	0.01 meter	=	cm

For students to fully understand the metric system, they must be forced to actually use it. Tape all of the combination meter/yardsticks in the classroom so the students can only see the metric measurement. Now have the students measure different areas of the room. A desk, a book, a floor tile, and so on. This will give the students a better appreciation of the measurement system. The same goes for any beakers that may have fluid ounces and liter measurements. Tape up the U.S. standard measures and force the students to use the metric measures.

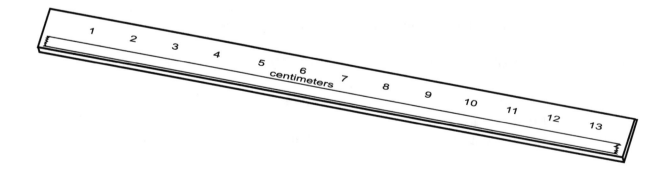

Name: _____ Date: _____

Metrics: *Metric Practice #1*

Directions: Measure the following bold lines and give the metric measure in decimeters, centimeters, and millimeters.

1. Decimeters: _____   Centimeters: _____   Millimeters: _____

2. Decimeters: _____   Centimeters: _____   Millimeters: _____

3. Decimeters: _____   Centimeters: _____   Millimeters: _____

4. Decimeters: _____   Centimeters: _____   Millimeters: _____

5. Decimeters: _____   Centimeters: _____   Millimeters: _____

Directions: Answer the following questions.

1. How many millimeters (mm) are in a meter (m)? _____

2. How many millimeters (mm) are in a decimeter (dm)? _____

3. How many millimeters (mm) are in a centimeter (cm)? _____

4. How many grams (g) are in a kilogram (kg)? _____

5. How many grams (g) are in a hectogram (hg)? _____

6. How many grams (g) are in a decagram (dag)? _____

Name: _____ Date: _____

Metrics: *Metric Practice #2*

Directions: Measure the following classroom items in centimeters. Then convert to millimeters and meters.

Item	Centimeters	Millimeters	Meters
1. Math book length	_____	_____	_____
2. Math book width	_____	_____	_____
3. Teacher's desk length	_____	_____	_____
4. Teacher's desk width	_____	_____	_____
5. Teacher's desk height	_____	_____	_____
6. Window width	_____	_____	_____
7. Window height	_____	_____	_____
8. Chalkboard height from floor	_____	_____	_____
9. Chalkboard length	_____	_____	_____
10. Chalkboard width	_____	_____	_____

Use the metric place value diagram below if needed to convert from centimeters to millimeters and meters.

____ ____ ____ ____ . ____ ____ ____
Kilo Hecto Deca Meter   Deci Centi Milli

Name: _____ Date: _____

Metrics: *Metric Practice #3*

Directions: Measure the following lengths of your body in centimeters. When completed, convert to millimeters and decimeters.

Body Part	Centimeters	Millimeters	Decimeters
1. Thumb length	_____	_____	_____
2. Forearm length (from elbow to finger tip)	_____	_____	_____
3. Foot length (from heel to big toe)	_____	_____	_____
4. Arm span length with arms out (from fingertip to fingertip)	_____	_____	_____
5. Height of knee from floor	_____	_____	_____
6. Height of yourself	_____	_____	_____
7. Length of one step from wall	_____	_____	_____
8. Arm length (from armpit to tip of finger)	_____	_____	_____
9. Leg length (from hip to floor)	_____	_____	_____
10. Length of big toe	_____	_____	_____

Use the metric place value diagram below if needed to convert from centimeters to millimeters and decimeters.

_____ _____ _____ _____ . _____ _____ _____
Kilo Hecto Deca Meter   Deci Centi Milli

Glossary

acute triangle: a triangle with all three angles less than 90°

addend: one of the numbers being added in an addition problem

addition: an adding of two or more numbers to get a number called the sum

base: the line or plane upon which a geometric figure is thought of as resting

centi: a metric prefix meaning "one-hundredth"

cone: a three-dimensional figure with a circular base and the top meeting at a vertex like a funnel

cylinder: a three-dimensional object with two circular bases like a can

deca (or deka): a metric prefix meaning "ten"

decagon: a ten-sided polygon

deci: a metric prefix meaning "one-tenth"

denominator: the term on the bottom of a fraction; it tells how many parts the whole is broken into

difference: the answer in a subtraction problem

dividend: the number being divided in a division problem

division: the process of finding how many times a number (the divisor) is contained in another number (the dividend); the result is the quotient

divisor: the number that is dividing the dividend in a division problem

dodecagon: a twelve-sided polygon

equilateral triangle: a triangle with all three sides of equal length

factor: one of the numbers being multiplied in a multiplication problem

fraction: a quantity expressed in terms of a numerator and denominator; it expresses the part of the whole present

gram: metric unit of measure for weight

hecto: a metric prefix meaning "one hundred"

heptagon: a seven-sided polygon

hexagon: a six-sided polygon

hexagonal pyramid: a pyramid with a hexagonal base

icosagon: a twenty-sided polygon

isosceles triangle: a triangle with at least two sides of exactly the same length

kilo: a metric prefix meaning "one thousand"

Glossary

 liter: metric unit of measure for volume or capacity

 meter: metric unit of measure for length

milli: a metric prefix meaning "one-thousandth"

minuend: the number from which another number (the subtrahend) is to be subtracted

multiplication: the process of finding the number obtained by repeated additions of a certain number a specified number of times

 nonagon: a nine-sided polygon

numerator: the term on the top of a fraction: it tells how many parts of the whole are present

 obtuse triangle: a triangle with one angle that measures more than 90°

octagon: an eight-sided polygon

order of operations: the established order in which mathematical operations are performed

 parallelogram: a quadrilateral with both pairs of opposite sides parallel

pentagonal prism: a prism with two pentagonal bases

pentagonal pyramid: a pyramid with a pentagonal base

place value: the value of a digit in a specific position in a number, such as the one's place, tenth's place, and so on

prefix: comes before the stem or unit in a metric measure and describes how large the unit actually is

prism: a three-dimensional object with rectangles for sides or faces

product: the answer in a multiplication problem

pyramid: a three-dimensional figure with triangles for sides or faces

 quadrilateral: a four-sided two-dimensional figure

quotient: the answer to a division problem

 rectangle: a parallelogram with 90° angles

rectangular prism: a prism with two rectangular bases

rectangular pyramid: a pyramid with a rectangular base

renaming (borrowing): in a subtraction problem when ten is borrowed from the next number to the left; the ten is added to the number being subtracted from so the subtraction can continue

renaming (carrying): in an addition problem when a number in the ten's place is carried to the next column to the left and is added to that column

Glossary

rhombus: a parallelogram with sides of equal length

right triangle: a triangle with one angle of exactly 90°

 scalene triangle: a triangle with all three sides of different lengths

sphere: a three-dimensional figure that is completely circular in width and height like a ball

square: a parallelogram with 90° angles and sides of equal length

stem: the unit name for a type of metric measure

subtraction: the process of finding the difference between two numbers

subtrahend: a number to be subtracted from another (the minuend)

sum: the answer in an addition problem

 trapezoid: a quadrilateral with only one pair of opposite sides parallel

triangle: a three-sided two-dimensional figure

triangular prism: a prism with two triangular bases

triangular pyramid: a pyramid with a triangular base

 undecagon: an eleven-sided polygon

vertices: plural of vertex; a corner point of a geometric figure

Name: _____

Student Addition Table

+	0	1	2	3	4	5	6	7	8	9
0										
1										
2										
3										
4										
5										
6										
7										
8										
9										

Addition Table

+	0	1	2	3	4	5	6	7	8	9
0	0	1	2	3	4	5	6	7	8	9
1	1	2	3	4	5	6	7	8	9	10
2	2	3	4	5	6	7	8	9	10	11
3	3	4	5	6	7	8	9	10	11	12
4	4	5	6	7	8	9	10	11	12	13
5	5	6	7	8	9	10	11	12	13	14
6	6	7	8	9	10	11	12	13	14	15
7	7	8	9	10	11	12	13	14	15	16
8	8	9	10	11	12	13	14	15	16	17
9	9	10	11	12	13	14	15	16	17	18

Subtraction Table

−	9	8	7	6	5	4	3	2	1	0
0	9	8	7	6	5	4	3	2	1	0
1	8	7	6	5	4	3	2	1	0	
2	7	6	5	4	3	2	1	0		
3	6	5	4	3	2	1	0			
4	5	4	3	2	1	0				
5	4	3	2	1	0					
6	3	2	1	0						
7	2	1	0							
8	1	0								
9	0									

Expanded Subtraction Table

−	10	11	12	13	14	15	16	17	18
9	1	2	3	4	5	6	7	8	9
8	2	3	4	5	6	7	8	9	
7	3	4	5	6	7	8	9		
6	4	5	6	7	8	9			
5	5	6	7	8	9				
4	6	7	8	9					
3	7	8	9						
2	8	9							
1	9								

Name: _____

Student Multiplication Table

x	1	2	3	4	5	6	7	8	9	10	11	12
1												
2												
3												
4												
5												
6												
7												
8												
9												
10												
11												
12												

Multiplication Table

×	1	2	3	4	5	6	7	8	9	10	11	12
1	1	2	3	4	5	6	7	8	9	10	11	12
2	2	4	6	8	10	12	14	16	18	20	22	24
3	3	6	9	12	15	18	21	24	27	30	33	36
4	4	8	12	16	20	24	28	32	36	40	44	48
5	5	10	15	20	25	30	35	40	45	50	55	60
6	6	12	18	24	30	36	42	48	54	60	66	72
7	7	14	21	28	35	42	49	56	63	70	77	84
8	8	16	24	32	40	48	56	64	72	80	88	96
9	9	18	27	36	45	54	63	72	81	90	99	108
10	10	20	30	40	50	60	70	80	90	100	110	120
11	11	22	33	44	55	66	77	88	99	110	121	132
12	12	24	36	48	60	72	84	96	108	120	132	144

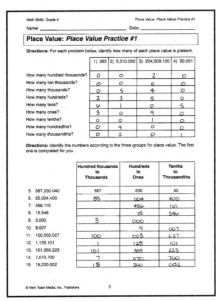
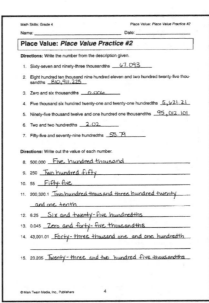
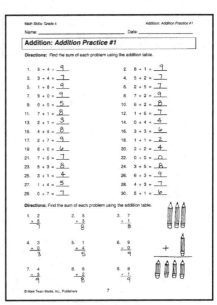
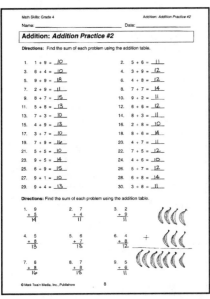
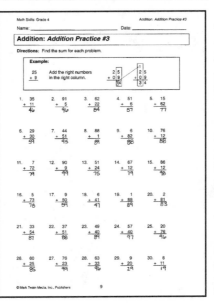
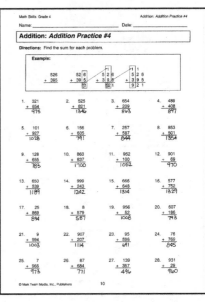
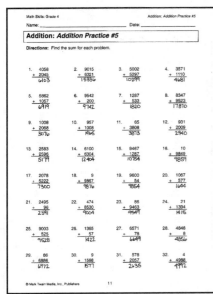
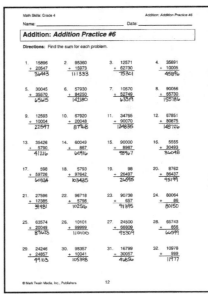
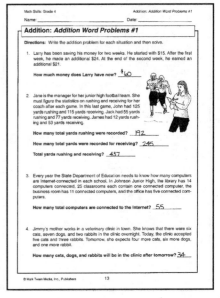

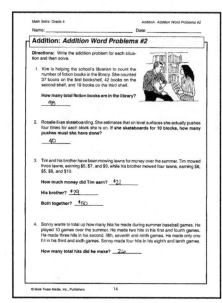

Name: _____ Date: _____

Addition: *Addition Word Problems #2*

Directions: Write the addition problem for each situation and then solve.

1. Kim is helping the school's librarian to count the number of fiction books in the library. She counted 37 books on the first bookshelf, 42 books on the second shelf, and 19 books on the third shelf.

   How many total fiction books are in the library? 98

2. Rosalie likes skateboarding. She estimates that on level surfaces she actually pushes four times for each block she is on. If she skateboards for 10 blocks, how many pushes must she have done? 40

3. Tim and his brother have been mowing lawns for money over the summer. Tim mowed three lawns, earning $5, $7, and $9, while his brother mowed four lawns, earning $6, $5, $8, and $10.

   How much money did Tim earn? $21

   His brother? $29

   Both together? $50

4. Sonny wants to total up how many hits he made during summer baseball games. He played 10 games over the summer. He made two hits in his first and fourth games. He made three hits in his second, fifth, seventh and ninth games. He made only one hit in his third and sixth games. Sonny made four hits in his eighth and tenth games.

   How many total hits did he make? 26

© Mark Twain Media, Inc., Publishers   14

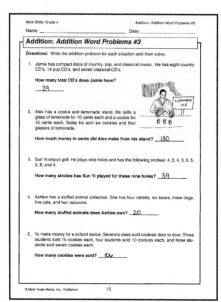

Addition: *Addition Word Problems #3*

Directions: Write the addition problem for each situation and then solve.

1. Jamie has compact discs of country, pop, and classical music. He has eight country CD's, 14 pop CD's, and seven classical CD's.

   How many total CD's does Jamie have? 29

2. Alex has a cookie and lemonade stand. He sells a glass of lemonade for 10 cents each and a cookie for 15 cents each. Today he sold six cookies and four glasses of lemonade.

   How much money in cents did Alex make from his stand? 130

3. Sun Yi enjoys golf. He plays nine holes and has the following strokes: 4, 5, 4, 3, 5, 5, 3, 6, and 4.

   How many strokes has Sun Yi played for these nine holes? 39

4. Ashlee has a stuffed animal collection. She has four rabbits, six bears, three dogs, five cats, and two raccoons.

   How many stuffed animals does Ashlee own? 20

5. To make money for a school dance, Serena's class sold cookies door to door. Three students sold 15 cookies each, four students sold 10 cookies each, and three students sold seven cookies each.

   How many cookies were sold? 106

© Mark Twain Media, Inc., Publishers   15

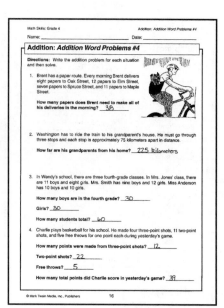

Addition: *Addition Word Problems #4*

Directions: Write the addition problem for each situation and then solve.

1. Brent has a paper route. Every morning Brent delivers eight papers to Oak Street, 12 papers to Elm Street, seven papers to Spruce Street, and 11 papers to Maple Street.

   How many papers does Brent need to make all of his deliveries in the morning? 38

2. Washington has to ride the train to his grandparent's house. He must go through three stops and each stop is approximately 75 kilometers apart in distance.

   How far are his grandparents from his home? 225 kilometers

3. In Wendy's school, there are three fourth-grade classes. In Mrs. Jones' class, there are 11 boys and eight girls. Mrs. Smith has nine boys and 12 girls. Miss Anderson has 10 boys and 10 girls.

   How many boys are in the fourth grade? 30

   Girls? 30

   How many students total? 60

4. Charlie plays basketball for his school. He made four three-point shots, 11 two-point shots, and five free throws for one point each during yesterday's game.

   How many points were made from three-point shots? 12

   Two-point shots? 22

   Free throws? 5

   How many total points did Charlie score in yesterday's game? 39

© Mark Twain Media, Inc., Publishers   16

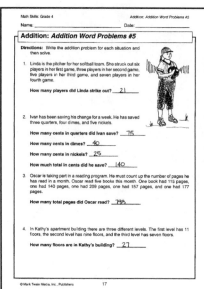

Addition: *Addition Word Problems #5*

Directions: Write the addition problem for each situation and then solve.

1. Linda is the pitcher for her softball team. She struck out six players in her first game, three players in her second game, five players in her third game, and seven players in her fourth game.

   How many players did Linda strike out? 21

2. Ivan has been saving his change for a week. He has saved three quarters, four dimes, and five nickels.

   How many cents in quarters did Ivan save? 75

   How many cents in dimes? 40

   How many cents in nickels? 25

   How much total in cents did he save? 140

3. Oscar is taking part in a reading program. He must count up the number of pages he has read in a month. Oscar read five books this month. One book had 115 pages, one had 140 pages, one had 209 pages, one had 157 pages, and one had 177 pages.

   How many total pages did Oscar read? 798

4. In Kathy's apartment building there are three different levels. The first level has 11 floors, the second level has nine floors, and the third level has seven floors.

   How many floors are in Kathy's building? 27

© Mark Twain Media, Inc., Publishers   17

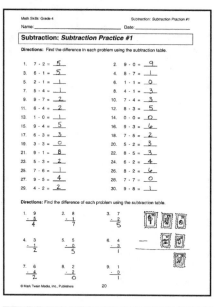

Subtraction: *Subtraction Practice #1*

Directions: Find the difference in each problem using the subtraction table.

1. 7 - 2 = 5		2. 9 - 0 = 9	
3. 6 - 1 = 5		4. 8 - 7 = 1	
5. 2 - 1 = 1		6. 1 - 1 = 0	
7. 5 - 4 = 1		8. 4 - 1 = 3	
9. 9 - 7 = 2		10. 7 - 4 = 3	
11. 6 - 4 = 2		12. 8 - 3 = 5	
13. 1 - 0 = 1		14. 0 - 0 = 0	
15. 9 - 4 = 5		16. 9 - 3 = 6	
17. 6 - 3 = 3		18. 7 - 5 = 2	
19. 3 - 3 = 0		20. 5 - 2 = 3	
21. 9 - 1 = 8		22. 8 - 5 = 3	
23. 5 - 3 = 2		24. 6 - 2 = 4	
25. 7 - 1 = 6		26. 8 - 2 = 6	
27. 9 - 5 = 4		28. 7 - 7 = 0	
29. 4 - 2 = 2		30. 9 - 8 = 1	

Directions: Find the difference of each problem using the subtraction table.

1. 9 - 5 = 4   2. 8 - 1 = 7   3. 7 - 2 = 5

4. 3 - 1 = 2   5. 5 - 0 = 5   6. 4 - 3 = 1

7. 6 - 4 = 2   8. 2 - 2 = 0   9. 1 - 0 = 1

© Mark Twain Media, Inc., Publishers   20

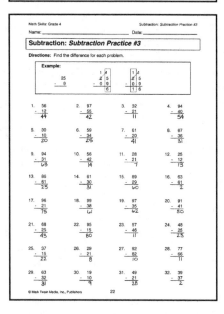

Subtraction: *Subtraction Practice #2*

Directions: Find the difference using the expanded subtraction table.

1. 18 - 9 = 9	2. 11 - 2 = 9
3. 17 - 9 = 8	4. 10 - 4 = 6
5. 16 - 8 = 8	6. 16 - 9 = 7
7. 15 - 9 = 6	8. 15 - 7 = 8
9. 14 - 7 = 7	10. 14 - 5 = 9
11. 13 - 6 = 7	12. 13 - 9 = 4
13. 13 - 8 = 5	14. 12 - 5 = 7
15. 11 - 4 = 7	16. 11 - 5 = 6
17. 10 - 9 = 1	18. 10 - 7 = 3
19. 17 - 8 = 9	20. 15 - 6 = 9
21. 16 - 7 = 9	22. 14 - 8 = 6
23. 15 - 8 = 7	24. 13 - 4 = 9
25. 14 - 6 = 8	26. 12 - 6 = 6
27. 13 - 5 = 8	28. 11 - 9 = 2
29. 12 - 8 = 4	30. 10 - 5 = 5

Directions: Find the difference using the expanded subtraction table.

1. 15   2. 17   3. 13
   - 6   - 9   - 8
     9   8   5

4. 11   5. 10   6. 16
   - 8   - 7   - 8
     3   3   8

7. 18   8. 14   9. 12
   - 9   - 6   - 7
     9   8   5

© Mark Twain Media, Inc., Publishers   21

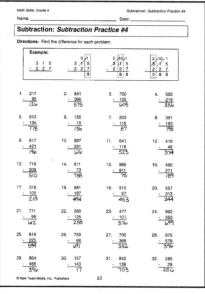

Subtraction: *Subtraction Practice #3*

Directions: Find the difference for each problem.

Example: 25 - 9 = 16

1. 56 - 12 = 44	2. 97 - 55 = 42	3. 32 - 21 = 11	4. 94 - 40 = 54
5. 30 - 10 = 20	6. 59 - 34 = 25	7. 61 - 20 = 41	8. 67 - 36 = 31
9. 94 - 31 = 63	10. 56 - 42 = 14	11. 28 - 21 = 7	12. 25 - 12 = 13
13. 86 - 61 = 25	14. 61 - 30 = 31	15. 89 - 29 = 60	16. 63 - 61 = 2
17. 96 - 21 = 75	18. 99 - 38 = 61	19. 97 - 35 = 62	20. 91 - 41 = 50
21. 68 - 25 = 43	22. 95 - 15 = 80	23. 57 - 46 = 11	24. 48 - 25 = 23
25. 37 - 15 = 22	26. 29 - 21 = 8	27. 92 - 82 = 10	28. 77 - 66 = 11
29. 63 - 32 = 31	30. 19 - 10 = 9	31. 49 - 21 = 28	32. 39 - 37 = 2

© Mark Twain Media, Inc., Publishers   22

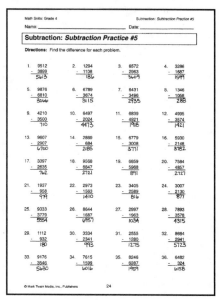

Subtraction: *Subtraction Practice #4*

Directions: Find the difference for each problem.

Example: 315 - 227 = 88

1. 211 - 85 = 126	2. 841 - 266 = 575	3. 730 - 125 = 605	4. 555 - 219 = 336
5. 912 - 134 = 778	6. 155 - 19 = 136	7. 203 - 116 = 87	8. 391 - 193 = 198
9. 617 - 421 = 196	10. 897 - 281 = 616	11. 641 - 118 = 523	12. 419 - 45 = 374
13. 719 - 209 = 510	14. 811 - 73 = 738	15. 986 - 911 = 75	16. 460 - 271 = 189
17. 318 - 105 = 213	18. 681 - 187 = 494	19. 510 - 57 = 453	20. 557 - 313 = 244
21. 711 - 99 = 612	22. 380 - 125 = 255	23. 477 - 101 = 376	24. 962 - 263 = 699
25. 819 - 225 = 594	26. 759 - 68 = 691	27. 700 - 368 = 332	28. 975 - 579 = 396
29. 864 - 468 = 396	30. 157 - 140 = 17	31. 842 - 139 = 703	32. 285 - 29 = 256

© Mark Twain Media, Inc., Publishers   23

Subtraction: *Subtraction Practice #5*

Directions: Find the difference for each problem.

1. 9512 - 3899 = 5613	2. 1294 - 1108 = 186	3. 6572 - 2963 = 3609	4. 3286 - 1687 = 1599
5. 9876 - 6810 = 3066	6. 6789 - 3674 = 3115	7. 6431 - 3496 = 2935	8. 1346 - 1068 = 288
9. 4210 - 3500 = 710	10. 6497 - 2024 = 4473	11. 6839 - 4921 = 1918	12. 4995 - 3574 = 1421
13. 9607 - 2907 = 6700	14. 2869 - 684 = 2185	15. 6779 - 3008 = 3771	16. 5930 - 2148 = 3782
17. 3397 - 2635 = 762	18. 9668 - 6847 = 2821	19. 6859 - 5968 = 891	20. 7584 - 4857 = 2727
21. 1937 - 958 = 979	22. 2973 - 1563 = 1410	23. 3405 - 2589 = 816	24. 3007 - 2130 = 877
25. 9333 - 3779 = 5554	26. 8644 - 1687 = 6957	27. 2997 - 1963 = 1034	28. 7893 - 3578 = 4315
29. 1112 - 932 = 180	30. 3334 - 2341 = 993	31. 2555 - 1280 = 1275	32. 8664 - 2941 = 5723
33. 9176 - 3546 = 5630	34. 7615 - 1599 = 6016	35. 8246 - 6287 = 1959	36. 6482 - 324 = 6158

© Mark Twain Media, Inc., Publishers   24

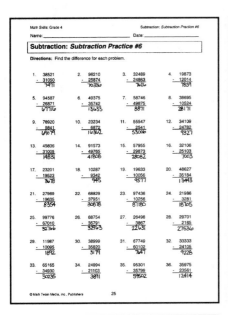

Subtraction: Subtraction Practice #6

Directions: Find the difference for each problem.

1. 38521 − 31050 = 7471	2. 96210 − 25874 = 70336	3. 32489 − 24863 = 7626	4. 19873 − 12014 = 7859
5. 94587 − 26871 = 67716	6. 49375 − 35742 = 13633	7. 58746 − 49875 = 8871	8. 38695 − 10524 = 28171
9. 78920 − 9841 = 69079	10. 23234 − 6872 = 16362	11. 55547 − 2541 = 53006	12. 34109 − 24782 = 9327
13. 45839 − 31005 = 14834	14. 91573 − 49785 = 41808	15. 57955 − 29873 = 28082	16. 32106 − 25103 = 7003
17. 23201 − 19523 = 3678	18. 10287 − 9342 = 945	19. 19633 − 10056 = 9577	20. 48627 − 35184 = 13443
21. 27989 − 19635 = 8354	22. 68829 − 37951 = 30878	23. 97436 − 10256 = 87180	24. 21986 − 3281 = 18705
25. 99776 − 67010 = 32766	26. 68754 − 35791 = 32963	27. 26496 − 3867 = 22631	28. 29701 − 2185 = 27536
29. 11987 − 10095 = 1892	30. 38999 − 35820 = 3179	31. 67749 − 60102 = 7647	32. 33333 − 24105 = 9228
33. 65165 − 34930 = 30235	34. 24994 − 21103 = 3891	35. 95301 − 35799 = 59502	36. 35975 − 23561 = 12414

© Mark Twain Media, Inc., Publishers   25

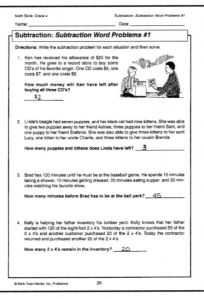

Subtraction: Subtraction Word Problems #1

Directions: Write the subtraction problem for each situation and then solve.

1. Ken has received his allowance of $20 for the month. He goes to a record store to buy some CD's of his favorite singer. One CD costs $5, one costs $7, and one costs $6.

   How much money will Ken have left after buying all three CD's? $2

2. Linda's beagle had seven puppies, and her black cat had nine kittens. She was able to give two puppies away to her friend Ashlee, three puppies to her friend Sam, and one puppy to her friend Stefanie. She was also able to give three kittens to her aunt Lucy, one kitten to her uncle Charlie, and three kittens to her cousin Brenda.

   How many puppies and kittens does Linda have left? 3

3. Brad has 120 minutes until he must be at the baseball game. He spends 15 minutes taking a shower, 10 minutes getting dressed, 20 minutes eating supper, and 30 minutes watching his favorite show.

   How many minutes before Brad has to be at the ball park? 45

4. Kelly is helping her father inventory his lumber yard. Kelly knows that her father started with 120 of the eight-foot 2 x 4's. Yesterday a contractor purchased 55 of the 2 x 4's and another customer purchased 20 of the 2 x 4's. Today the contractor returned and purchased another 25 of the 2 x 4's.

   How many 2 x 4's remain in the inventory? 20

© Mark Twain Media, Inc., Publishers   26

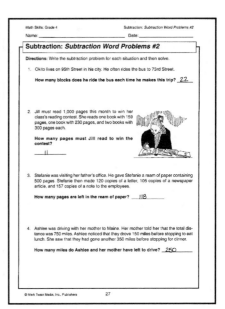

Subtraction: Subtraction Word Problems #2

Directions: Write the subtraction problem for each situation and then solve.

1. Okito lives on 95th Street in his city. He often rides the bus to 73rd Street.

   How many blocks does he ride the bus each time he makes this trip? 22

2. Jill must read 1,000 pages this month to win her class's reading contest. She reads one book with 159 pages, one book with 230 pages, and two books with 300 pages each.

   How many pages must Jill read to win the contest? 11

3. Stefanie was visiting her father's office. He gave Stefanie a ream of paper containing 500 pages. Stefanie then made 120 copies of a letter, 105 copies of a newspaper article, and 157 copies of a note to the employees.

   How many pages are left in the ream of paper? 118

4. Ashlee was driving with her mother to Maine. Her mother told her that the total distance was 750 miles. Ashlee noticed that they drove 150 miles before stopping to eat lunch. She saw that they had gone another 350 miles before stopping for dinner.

   How many miles do Ashlee and her mother have left to drive? 250

© Mark Twain Media, Inc., Publishers   27

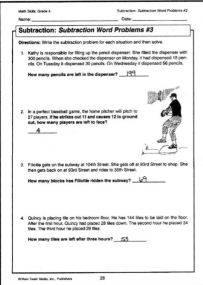

Subtraction: Subtraction Word Problems #3

Directions: Write the subtraction problem for each situation and then solve.

1. Kathy is responsible for filling up the pencil dispenser. She filled the dispenser with 300 pencils. When she checked the dispenser on Monday, it had dispensed 15 pencils. On Tuesday it dispensed 30 pencils. On Wednesday it dispensed 56 pencils.

   How many pencils are left in the dispenser? 199

2. In a perfect baseball game, the home pitcher will pitch to 27 players. If he strikes out 11 and causes 12 to ground out, how many players are left to face? 4

3. Filicitie gets on the subway at 104th Street. She gets off at 93rd Street to shop. She then gets back on at 93rd Street and rides to 35th Street.

   How many blocks has Filicitie ridden the subway? 69

4. Quincy is placing tile on his bedroom floor. He has 144 tiles to be laid on the floor. After the first hour, Quincy had placed 28 tiles down. The second hour he placed 34 tiles. The third hour he placed 29 tiles.

   How many tiles are left after three hours? 53

© Mark Twain Media, Inc., Publishers   28

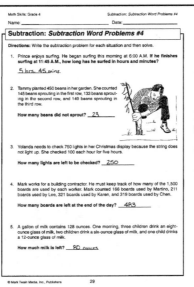

Subtraction: Subtraction Word Problems #4

Directions: Write the subtraction problem for each situation and then solve.

1. Prince enjoys surfing. He began surfing this morning at 6:00 A.M. If he finishes surfing at 11:45 A.M., how long has he surfed in hours and minutes? 5 hrs. 45 mins.

2. Tammy planted 450 beans in her garden. She counted 145 beans sprouting in the first row, 133 beans sprouting in the second row, and 149 beans sprouting in the third row.

   How many beans did not sprout? 23

3. Yolanda needs to check 750 lights in her Christmas display because the string does not light up. She checked 100 each hour for five hours.

   How many lights are left to be checked? 250

4. Mark works for a building contractor. He must keep track of how many of the 1,500 boards are used by each worker. Mark counted 166 boards used by Martino, 211 boards used by Lee, 321 boards used by Karen, and 319 boards used by Chen.

   How many boards are left at the end of the day? 483

5. A gallon of milk contains 128 ounces. One morning, three children drink an eight-ounce glass of milk, two children drink a six-ounce glass of milk, and one child drinks a 12-ounce glass of milk.

   How much milk is left? 80 ounces

© Mark Twain Media, Inc., Publishers   29

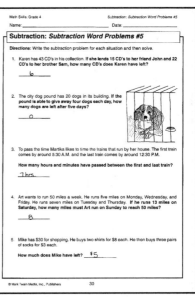

Subtraction: Subtraction Word Problems #5

Directions: Write the subtraction problem for each situation and then solve.

1. Karen has 43 CD's in his collection. If she lends 15 CD's to her friend John and 22 CD's to her brother Sam, how many CD's does Karen have left? 6

2. The city dog pound has 20 dogs in its building. If the pound is able to give away four dogs each day, how many dogs are left after five days? 0

3. To pass the time Martika likes to time the trains that run by her house. The first train comes by around 5:30 A.M. and the last train comes by around 12:30 P.M.

   How many hours and minutes have passed between the first and last train? 7 hrs.

4. Art wants to run 50 miles a week. He runs five miles on Monday, Wednesday, and Friday. He runs seven miles on Tuesday and Thursday. If he runs 13 miles on Saturday, how many miles must Art run on Sunday to reach 50 miles? 8

5. Mike has $30 for shopping. He buys two shirts for $8 each. He then buys three pairs of socks for $3 each.

   How much does Mike have left? $5

© Mark Twain Media, Inc., Publishers   30

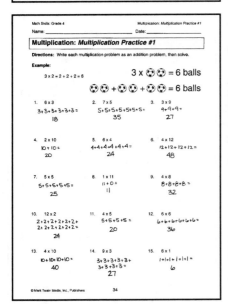

Multiplication: Multiplication Practice #1

Directions: Write each multiplication problem as an addition problem, then solve.

Example:

3 x 2 = 2 + 2 + 2 = 6

3 x ⚽⚽ = 6 balls

⚽⚽ + ⚽⚽ + ⚽⚽ = 6 balls

1. 6 x 3
3+3+3+3+3+3 = 18

2. 7 x 5
5+5+5+5+5+5+5 = 35

3. 3 x 9
9+9+9 = 27

4. 2 x 10
10 + 10 = 20

5. 6 x 4
4+4+4+4+4+4 = 24

6. 4 x 12
12+12+12+12 = 48

7. 5 x 5
5+5+5+5+5 = 25

8. 1 x 11
11 + 0 = 11

9. 4 x 8
8+8+8+8 = 32

10. 12 x 2
2+2+2+2+2+2+2+2+2+2+2+2 = 24

11. 4 x 5
5+5+5+5 = 20

12. 6 x 6
6+6+6+6+6+6 = 36

13. 4 x 10
10+10+10+10 = 40

14. 9 x 3
3+3+3+3+3+3+3+3+3 = 27

15. 6 x 1
1+1+1+1+1+1 = 6

© Mark Twain Media, Inc., Publishers   34

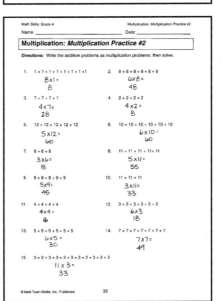

Multiplication: Multiplication Practice #2

Directions: Write the addition problems as multiplication problems, then solve.

1. 1+1+1+1+1+1+1+1
8 x 1 = 8

2. 8+8+8+8+9+8
6 x 8 = 48

3. 7+7+7+7
4 x 7 = 28

4. 2+2+2+2
4 x 2 = 8

5. 12+12+12+12+12
5 x 12 = 60

6. 10+10+10+10+10+10
6 x 10 = 60

7. 6+6+6
3 x 6 = 18

8. 11+11+11+11+11
5 x 11 = 55

9. 9+9+9+9+9
5 x 9 = 45

10. 11+11+11
3 x 11 = 33

11. 4+4+4+4
4 x 4 = 16

12. 3+3+3+3+3+3
6 x 3 = 18

13. 5+5+5+5+5+5
6 x 5 = 30

14. 7+7+7+7+7+7+7
7 x 7 = 49

15. 3+3+3+3+3+3+3+3+3+3+3
11 x 3 = 33

© Mark Twain Media, Inc., Publishers   35

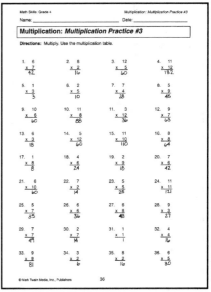

Multiplication: Multiplication Practice #3

Directions: Multiply. Use the multiplication table.

1. 6 x 7 = 42	2. 8 x 2 = 16	3. 12 x 5 = 60	4. 11 x 12 = 132
5. 1 x 3 = 3	6. 2 x 5 = 10	7. 7 x 4 = 28	8. 5 x 9 = 45
9. 10 x 6 = 60	10. 11 x 8 = 88	11. 3 x 12 = 36	12. 9 x 7 = 63
13. 6 x 3 = 18	14. 5 x 12 = 60	15. 11 x 10 = 110	16. 8 x 8 = 64
17. 1 x 8 = 8	18. 4 x 6 = 24	19. 2 x 9 = 18	20. 6 x 7 = 42
21. 6 x 10 = 60	22. 2 x 7 = 14	23. 5 x 5 = 25	24. 11 x 11 = 121
25. 5 x 7 = 35	26. 6 x 6 = 36	27. 8 x 6 = 48	28. 9 x 3 = 27
29. 7 x 7 = 49	30. 2 x 7 = 14	31. 1 x 1 = 1	32. 4 x 4 = 16
33. 9 x 9 = 81	34. 3 x 2 = 6	35. 8 x 2 = 16	36. 6 x 5 = 30

© Mark Twain Media, Inc., Publishers   36

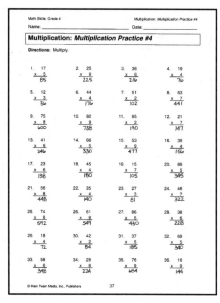

Multiplication Practice #4 (page 37)

Directions: Multiply.

1. 17 × 5 = 85
2. 25 × 9 = 225
3. 36 × 6 = 216
4. 19 × 4 = 76
5. 12 × 3 = 36
6. 44 × 4 = 176
7. 51 × 2 = 102
8. 63 × 7 = 441
9. 75 × 8 = 600
10. 82 × 9 = 738
11. 95 × 2 = 190
12. 21 × 7 = 147
13. 41 × 6 = 246
14. 66 × 5 = 330
15. 53 × 9 = 477
16. 39 × 4 = 156
17. 41 × 6 = 138
18. 45 × 4 = 180
19. 15 × 7 = 105
20. 69 × 5 = 345
21. 56 × 8 = 448
22. 35 × 4 = 140
23. 27 × 3 = 81
24. 46 × 7 = 322
25. 74 × 8 = 592
26. 61 × 9 = 549
27. 86 × 5 = 430
28. 38 × 6 = 228
29. 18 × 4 = 72
30. 42 × 2 = 84
31. 37 × 5 = 185
32. 68 × 5 = 340
33. 58 × 6 = 348
34. 28 × 8 = 224
35. 76 × 9 = 684
36. 16 × 9 = 144

Multiplication Practice #5 (page 38)

Directions: Multiply. Show each multiplication step.

Example:
15 × 24 = 360

1. 16 × 35 = 560
2. 99 × 16 = 1584
3. 84 × 43 = 3612
4. 72 × 51 = 3672
5. 29 × 88 = 2552
6. 54 × 78 = 4212
7. 44 × 57 = 2508
8. 67 × 94 = 6298
9. 37 × 24 = 888
10. 13 × 18 = 234
11. 29 × 28 = 812
12. 39 × 39 = 1521
13. 41 × 21 = 861
14. 71 × 30 = 2130
15. 68 × 57 = 3876
16. 38 × 85 = 3230
17. 60 × 11 = 660
18. 59 × 15 = 885
19. 32 × 32 = 1024
20. 28 × 29 = 812

Multiplication Practice #6 (page 39)

Directions: Multiply.

1. 127 × 2 = 254
2. 257 × 8 = 2056
3. 645 × 7 = 4515
4. 279 × 3 = 837
5. 167 × 3 = 501
6. 498 × 6 = 2988
7. 455 × 7 = 3185
8. 287 × 9 = 2583
9. 962 × 7 = 6734
10. 853 × 6 = 5118
11. 743 × 5 = 3715
12. 199 × 4 = 796
13. 210 × 4 = 840
14. 333 × 2 = 666
15. 348 × 5 = 1740
16. 781 × 3 = 2343
17. 987 × 9 = 8883
18. 456 × 4 = 1824
19. 226 × 8 = 1808
20. 645 × 5 = 3225
21. 317 × 9 = 2853
22. 784 × 8 = 6272
23. 618 × 5 = 3090
24. 733 × 7 = 5131
25. 555 × 8 = 4440
26. 574 × 5 = 2870
27. 488 × 6 = 2928
28. 884 × 3 = 2652
29. 399 × 3 = 1197
30. 686 × 6 = 4116
31. 717 × 4 = 2848
32. 813 × 2 = 1626
33. 221 × 3 = 663
34. 300 × 8 = 2400
35. 607 × 9 = 5463
36. 905 × 7 = 6335

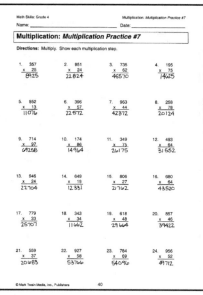

Multiplication Practice #7 (page 40)

Directions: Multiply. Show each multiplication step.

1. 357 × 25 = 8925
2. 951 × 24 = 22,824
3. 735 × 62 = 45570
4. 195 × 75 = 14625
5. 852 × 13 = 11076
6. 396 × 57 = 22,572
7. 963 × 44 = 42372
8. 258 × 78 = 20124
9. 714 × 97 = 69258
10. 174 × 86 = 14964
11. 349 × 75 = 26175
12. 493 × 64 = 31552
13. 946 × 24 = 22704
14. 649 × 19 = 12,331
15. 806 × 27 = 21762
16. 680 × 64 = 43520
17. 779 × 33 = 25707
18. 343 × 34 = 11662
19. 618 × 48 = 29664
20. 857 × 46 = 39422
21. 559 × 37 = 20683
22. 927 × 58 = 53766
23. 784 × 69 = 54096
24. 956 × 52 = 49712

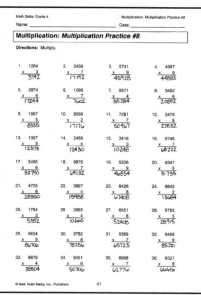

Multiplication Practice #8 (page 41)

Directions: Multiply.

1. 1264 × 3 = 3792
2. 2456 × 7 = 17192
3. 5741 × 8 = 45928
4. 4987 × 9 = 44883
5. 2874 × 6 = 17244
6. 1086 × 7 = 7602
7. 9571 × 4 = 38284
8. 3482 × 6 = 20892
9. 1667 × 5 = 8335
10. 8588 × 2 = 17176
11. 7281 × 7 = 50967
12. 3479 × 8 = 27832
13. 1397 × 9 = 12573
14. 2486 × 5 = 12430
15. 3416 × 3 = 10248
16. 9746 × 7 = 68222
17. 5465 × 6 = 32790
18. 9876 × 7 = 69132
19. 5206 × 9 = 46854
20. 6347 × 5 = 31735
21. 4725 × 6 = 28350
22. 3997 × 4 = 15988
23. 8426 × 8 = 67408
24. 6842 × 2 = 13684
25. 1784 × 3 = 5352
26. 2665 × 4 = 10660
27. 6551 × 8 = 52408
28. 5783 × 5 = 28915
29. 9634 × 9 = 86706
30. 9782 × 8 = 78256
31. 9389 × 7 = 65723
32. 9469 × 9 = 85221
33. 8876 × 4 = 35504
34. 8451 × 6 = 50706
35. 8968 × 7 = 62776
36. 8327 × 8 = 66616

Multiplication Practice #9 (page 42)

Directions: Multiply. Show each multiplication step.

1. 5524 × 97 = 535828
2. 6057 × 52 = 315534
3. 8991 × 46 = 413586
4. 3425 × 31 = 106175
5. 5103 × 92 = 469476
6. 6741 × 83 = 559503
7. 4187 × 79 = 329193
8. 9467 × 64 = 605888
9. 2583 × 61 = 157563
10. 5832 × 42 = 244944
11. 8352 × 72 = 601344
12. 3852 × 81 = 312012
13. 3971 × 91 = 361361
14. 9713 × 62 = 602206
15. 7139 × 84 = 599676
16. 1397 × 95 = 132715
17. 6793 × 63 = 427959
18. 8623 × 52 = 448396
19. 3046 × 85 = 258910
20. 8709 × 74 = 644466
21. 2240 × 32 = 71680
22. 5566 × 54 = 300564
23. 8844 × 87 = 769428
24. 9993 × 65 = 649545

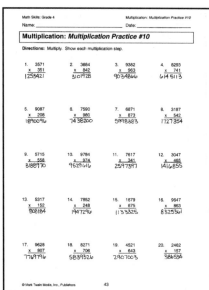

Multiplication Practice #10 (page 43)

Directions: Multiply. Show each multiplication step.

1. 3571 × 351 = 1253421
2. 3684 × 842 = 3101928
3. 9382 × 963 = 9034866
4. 8293 × 741 = 6145113
5. 9087 × 208 = 1890096
6. 7590 × 980 = 7438200
7. 6871 × 873 = 5998383
8. 3187 × 542 = 1727354
9. 5715 × 558 = 3188970
10. 9784 × 974 = 9529616
11. 7617 × 341 = 2597397
12. 3047 × 465 = 1416855
13. 5317 × 152 = 808184
14. 7852 × 248 = 1947296
15. 1879 × 675 = 1133325
16. 9647 × 863 = 8325361
17. 9628 × 807 = 7769796
18. 8271 × 706 = 5839326
19. 4521 × 643 = 2907003
20. 2462 × 157 = 386534

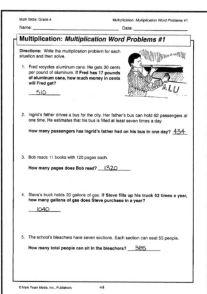

Multiplication Word Problems #1 (page 44)

Directions: Write the multiplication problem for each situation and then solve.

1. Fred recycles aluminum cans. He gets 30 cents per pound of aluminum. If Fred has 17 pounds of aluminum cans, how much money in cents will Fred get? **510**

2. Ingrid's father drives a bus for the city. Her father's bus can hold 62 passengers at one time. He estimates that his bus is filled at least seven times a day.
How many passengers has Ingrid's father had on his bus in one day? **434**

3. Bob reads 11 books with 120 pages each.
How many pages does Bob read? **1320**

4. Steve's truck holds 20 gallons of gas. If Steve fills up his truck 52 times a year, how many gallons of gas does Steve purchase in a year? **1040**

5. The school's bleachers have seven sections. Each section can seat 55 people.
How many total people can sit in the bleachers? **385**

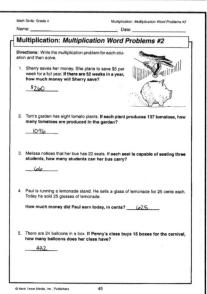

Multiplication Word Problems #2 (page 45)

Directions: Write the multiplication problem for each situation and then solve.

1. Sherry saves her money. She plans to save $5 per week for a full year. If there are 52 weeks in a year, how much money will Sherry save? **$260**

2. Tom's garden has eight tomato plants. If each plant produces 137 tomatoes, how many tomatoes are produced in the garden? **1096**

3. Melissa notices that her bus has 22 seats. If each seat is capable of seating three students, how many students can her bus carry? **66**

4. Paul is running a lemonade stand. He sells a glass of lemonade for 25 cents each. Today he sold 25 glasses of lemonade.
How much money did Paul earn today, in cents? **625**

5. There are 24 balloons in a box. If Penny's class buys 18 boxes for the carnival, how many balloons does her class have? **432**

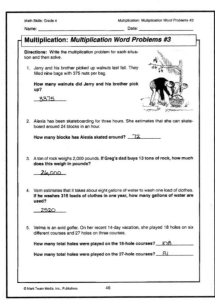

Multiplication: Multiplication Word Problems #3

Directions: Write the multiplication problem for each situation and then solve.

1. Jerry and his brother picked up walnuts last fall. They filled nine bags with 375 nuts per bag.

   How many walnuts did Jerry and his brother pick up?

   3375

2. Alexia has been skateboarding for three hours. She estimates that she can skateboard around 24 blocks in an hour.

   How many blocks has Alexia skated around? 72

3. A ton of rock weighs 2,000 pounds. If Greg's dad buys 13 tons of rock, how much does this weigh in pounds?

   26,000

4. Vern estimates that it takes about eight gallons of water to wash one load of clothes. If he washes 315 loads of clothes in one year, how many gallons of water are used?

   2520

5. Velma is an avid golfer. On her recent 14-day vacation, she played 18 holes on six different courses and 27 holes on three courses.

   How many total holes were played on the 18-hole courses? 108

   How many total holes were played on the 27-hole courses? 81

© Mark Twain Media, Inc., Publishers 46

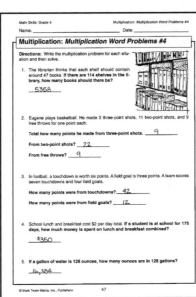

Multiplication: Multiplication Word Problems #4

Directions: Write the multiplication problem for each situation and then solve.

1. The librarian thinks that each shelf should contain around 47 books. If there are 114 shelves in the library, how many books should there be?

   5358

2. Eugene plays basketball. He made 3 three-point shots, 11 two-point shots, and 9 free throws for one point each.

   Total how many points he made from three-point shots. 9

   From two-point shots? 22

   From free throws? 9

3. In football, a touchdown is worth six points. A field goal is three points. A team scores seven touchdowns and four field goals.

   How many points were from touchdowns? 42

   How many points were from field goals? 12

4. School lunch and breakfast cost $2 per day total. If a student is at school for 175 days, how much money is spent on lunch and breakfast combined?

   $350

5. If a gallon of water is 128 ounces, how many ounces are in 128 gallons?

   16,384

© Mark Twain Media, Inc., Publishers 47

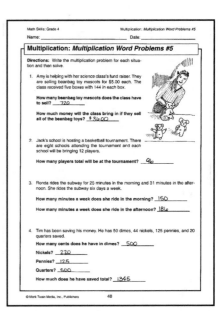

Multiplication: Multiplication Word Problems #5

Directions: Write the multiplication problem for each situation and then solve.

1. Amy is helping with her science class's fund raiser. They are selling beanbag toy mascots for $5.00 each. The class received five boxes with 144 in each box.

   How many beanbag toy mascots does the class have to sell? 720

   How much money will the class bring in if they sell all of the beanbag toys? $3600

2. Jack's school is hosting a basketball tournament. There are eight schools attending the tournament and each school will be bringing 12 players.

   How many players total will be at the tournament? 96

3. Ronda rides the subway for 25 minutes in the morning and 31 minutes in the afternoon. She rides the subway six days a week.

   How many minutes a week does she ride in the morning? 150

   How many minutes a week does she ride in the afternoon? 186

4. Tim has been saving his money. He has 50 dimes, 44 nickels, 125 pennies, and 20 quarters saved.

   How many cents does he have in dimes? 500

   Nickels? 220

   Pennies? 125

   Quarters? 500

   How much does he have saved total? 1345

© Mark Twain Media, Inc., Publishers 48

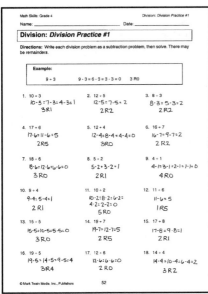

Division: Division Practice #1

Directions: Write each division problem as a subtraction problem, then solve. There may be remainders.

Example:
9 ÷ 3   9-3=6-3=3-3=0   3 R0

1. 10 ÷ 3
   10-3=7-3=4-3=1
   3R1

2. 12 ÷ 5
   12-5=7-5=2
   2R2

3. 8 ÷ 3
   8-3=5-3=2
   2R2

4. 17 ÷ 6
   17-6=11-6=5
   2R5

5. 12 ÷ 4
   12-4=8-4=4-4=0
   3R0

6. 16 ÷ 7
   16-7=9-7=2
   2 R2

7. 18 ÷ 6
   18-6=12-6=6-6=0
   3R0

8. 5 ÷ 2
   5-2=3-2+1
   2R1

9. 4 ÷ 1
   4-1=3-1=2-1=1-1=0
   4R0

10. 9 ÷ 4
    9-4=5-4=1
    2 R1

11. 10 ÷ 2
    10-2=8-2=6-2=
    4-2=2-2=0
    5R0

12. 11 ÷ 6
    11-6=5
    1R5

13. 15 ÷ 5
    15-5=10-5=5-5=0
    3R0

14. 19 ÷ 7
    19-7=12-7=5
    2R5

15. 17 ÷ 8
    17-8=9-8=1
    2R1

16. 19 ÷ 5
    19-5=14-5=9-5=4
    3R4

17. 12 ÷ 6
    12-6=6-6=0
    2 R0

18. 14 ÷ 4
    14-4=10-4=6-4=2
    3 R2

© Mark Twain Media, Inc., Publishers 52

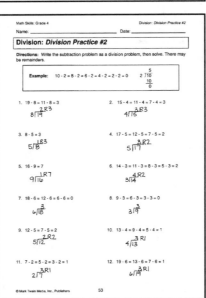

Division: Division Practice #2

Directions: Write the subtraction problem as a division problem, then solve. There may be remainders.

Example: 10-2=8-2=6-2=4-2=2-2=0   5 / 2⟌10 10 0

1. 19 - 8 = 11 - 8 = 3
   2R3 8⟌19

2. 15 - 4 = 11 - 4 = 7 - 4 = 3
   3R3 4⟌15

3. 8 - 5 = 3
   1R3 5⟌8

4. 17 - 5 = 12 - 5 = 7 - 5 = 2
   3R2 5⟌17

5. 16 - 9 = 7
   1R7 9⟌16

6. 14 - 3 = 11 - 3 = 8 - 3 = 5 - 3 = 2
   4R2 3⟌14

7. 18 - 6 = 12 - 6 = 6 - 6 = 0
   3 6⟌18

8. 9 - 3 = 6 - 3 = 3 - 3 = 0
   3 3⟌9

9. 12 - 5 = 7 - 5 = 2
   2R2 5⟌12

10. 13 - 4 = 9 - 4 = 5 - 4 = 1
    3R1 4⟌13

11. 7 - 2 = 5 - 2 = 3 - 2 = 1
    3R1 2⟌7

12. 19 - 6 = 13 - 6 = 7 - 6 = 1
    3R1 6⟌19

© Mark Twain Media, Inc., Publishers 53

Division: Division Practice #3

Directions: Divide. Use the multiplication table.

1. 5⟌1 1
2. 2⟌8 4
3. 3⟌6 2
4. 2⟌2 1
5. 1⟌6 6
6. 4⟌8 2
7. 1⟌7 7
8. 7⟌1 1
9. 2⟌6 3
10. 1⟌8 8
11. 3⟌9 3
12. 2⟌0 0
13. 3⟌15 5
14. 9⟌18 2
15. 10⟌90 9

© Mark Twain Media, Inc., Publishers 54

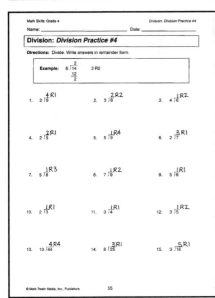

Division: Division Practice #4

Directions: Divide. Write answers in remainder form.

Example: 6⟌14 12 2   2 R2

1. 2⟌9 4 R1
2. 3⟌8 2 R2
3. 4⟌6 1 R2
4. 2⟌5 2 R1
5. 5⟌9 1 R4
6. 2⟌7 3 R1
7. 5⟌8 1 R3
8. 7⟌9 1 R2
9. 5⟌6 1 R1
10. 2⟌3 1 R1
11. 3⟌4 1 R1
12. 3⟌5 1 R2
13. 10⟌44 4 R4
14. 8⟌25 3 R1
15. 3⟌16 5 R1

© Mark Twain Media, Inc., Publishers 55

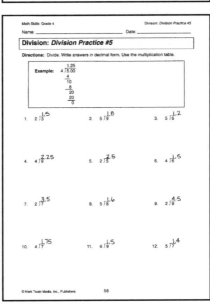

Division: Division Practice #5

Directions: Divide. Write answers in decimal form. Use the multiplication table.

Example: 4⟌5.00 1.25 4 10 8 20 20 0

1. 2⟌3 1.5
2. 5⟌9 1.8
3. 5⟌6 1.2
4. 4⟌9 2.25
5. 2⟌5 2.5
6. 4⟌6 1.5
7. 2⟌7 3.5
8. 5⟌8 1.6
9. 2⟌9 4.5
10. 4⟌7 1.75
11. 6⟌9 1.5
12. 5⟌7 1.4

© Mark Twain Media, Inc., Publishers 56

Division: Division Practice #6

Directions: Divide. Write answers in remainder form if required.

1. 5⟌19 3 R4
2. 2⟌22 11
3. 5⟌41 8 R1
4. 6⟌63 10 R3
5. 6⟌71 11 R5
6. 8⟌51 6 R3
7. 6⟌18 3
8. 8⟌29 3 R5
9. 9⟌35 3 R8
10. 4⟌46 11 R2
11. 3⟌52 17 R1
12. 4⟌64 16
13. 8⟌82 10 R2
14. 8⟌95 11 R7
15. 9⟌76 8 R4

© Mark Twain Media, Inc., Publishers 57

Division: Division Practice #7

Directions: Divide. Write answers in decimal form if required.

1. $5\overline{)31} = 6.2$
2. $5\overline{)42} = 8.4$
3. $6\overline{)57} = 9.5$
4. $6\overline{)75} = 12.5$
5. $9\overline{)63} = 7$
6. $5\overline{)32} = 6.4$
7. $6\overline{)54} = 9$
8. $5\overline{)61} = 12.2$
9. $8\overline{)60} = 7.5$
10. $5\overline{)41} = 8.2$
11. $5\overline{)65} = 13$
12. $6\overline{)69} = 11.5$
13. $8\overline{)98} = 12.25$
14. $4\overline{)37} = 9.25$
15. $8\overline{)64} = 8$

58

Division: Division Practice #8

Directions: Divide. Write answers in remainder form if required.

1. $21\overline{)96} = 4\,R12$
2. $25\overline{)85} = 3\,R10$
3. $17\overline{)63} = 3\,R12$
4. $11\overline{)24} = 2\,R2$
5. $15\overline{)65} = 4\,R5$
6. $19\overline{)79} = 4\,R3$
7. $12\overline{)48} = 4$
8. $18\overline{)64} = 3\,R10$
9. $33\overline{)97} = 2\,R31$
10. $31\overline{)86} = 2\,R24$
11. $24\overline{)72} = 3$
12. $17\overline{)66} = 3\,R15$
13. $24\overline{)59} = 2\,R11$
14. $15\overline{)36} = 2\,R6$
15. $16\overline{)80} = 5$

59

Division: Division Practice #9

Directions: Divide. Write answers in decimal form if required.

1. $15\overline{)96} = 6.4$
2. $10\overline{)63} = 6.3$
3. $24\overline{)78} = 3.25$
4. $18\overline{)81} = 4.5$
5. $12\overline{)90} = 7.5$
6. $18\overline{)99} = 5.5$
7. $17\overline{)68} = 4$
8. $15\overline{)93} = 6.2$
9. $31\overline{)93} = 3$
10. $12\overline{)75} = 6.25$
11. $29\overline{)87} = 3$
12. $16\overline{)84} = 5.25$
13. $25\overline{)80} = 3.2$
14. $16\overline{)34} = 2.125$
15. $24\overline{)75} = 3.125$

60

Division: Division Practice #10

Directions: Divide. Write answers in remainder form if required.

1. $6\overline{)125} = 20\,R5$
2. $8\overline{)492} = 61\,R4$
3. $7\overline{)612} = 87\,R3$
4. $9\overline{)830} = 92\,R2$
5. $3\overline{)186} = 62$
6. $9\overline{)294} = 32\,R6$
7. $5\overline{)525} = 105$
8. $6\overline{)810} = 135$
9. $7\overline{)372} = 53\,R1$
10. $8\overline{)729} = 91\,R1$
11. $7\overline{)265} = 37\,R6$
12. $4\overline{)408} = 102$
13. $3\overline{)921} = 307$
14. $2\overline{)831} = 415\,R1$
15. $4\overline{)619} = 154\,R3$

61

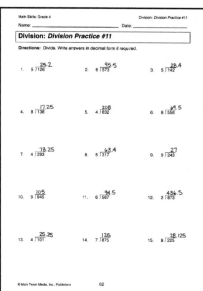

Division: Division Practice #11

Directions: Divide. Write answers in decimal form if required.

1. $5\overline{)126} = 25.2$
2. $6\overline{)573} = 95.5$
3. $5\overline{)142} = 28.4$
4. $8\overline{)138} = 17.25$
5. $4\overline{)832} = 208$
6. $8\overline{)556} = 69.5$
7. $4\overline{)293} = 73.25$
8. $5\overline{)317} = 63.4$
9. $9\overline{)243} = 27$
10. $9\overline{)945} = 105$
11. $6\overline{)567} = 94.5$
12. $2\overline{)873} = 436.5$
13. $4\overline{)101} = 25.25$
14. $7\overline{)875} = 125$
15. $8\overline{)225} = 28.125$

62

Division: Division Practice #12

Directions: Divide. Write answers in remainder form if required.

1. $26\overline{)690} = 26\,R14$
2. $45\overline{)966} = 21\,R21$
3. $50\overline{)758} = 15\,R8$
4. $31\overline{)631} = 20\,R11$
5. $61\overline{)549} = 9$
6. $33\overline{)770} = 23\,R11$
7. $94\overline{)990} = 10\,R50$
8. $75\overline{)999} = 13\,R24$
9. $81\overline{)900} = 11\,R9$
10. $73\overline{)438} = 6$
11. $15\overline{)232} = 15\,R7$
12. $27\overline{)967} = 35\,R22$
13. $65\overline{)395} = 6\,R5$
14. $19\overline{)390} = 20\,R10$
15. $44\overline{)264} = 6$

63

Division: Division Practice #13

Directions: Divide. Write answers in decimal form if required.

1. $24\overline{)318} = 13.25$
2. $30\overline{)615} = 20.5$
3. $62\overline{)930} = 15$
4. $15\overline{)243} = 16.2$
5. $16\overline{)156} = 9.75$
6. $28\overline{)483} = 17.25$
7. $21\overline{)756} = 36$
8. $36\overline{)234} = 6.5$
9. $76\overline{)665} = 8.75$
10. $72\overline{)846} = 11.75$
11. $14\overline{)406} = 29$
12. $48\overline{)732} = 15.25$
13. $48\overline{)294} = 6.125$
14. $80\overline{)684} = 8.55$
15. $56\overline{)511} = 9.125$

64

Division: Division Practice #14

Directions: Divide. Write answers in remainder form if required.

1. $9\overline{)3213} = 357$
2. $7\overline{)3402} = 486$
3. $6\overline{)3915} = 652\,R3$
4. $5\overline{)1477} = 295\,R2$
5. $8\overline{)3287} = 410\,R7$
6. $4\overline{)1501} = 375\,R1$
7. $7\overline{)1550} = 221\,R3$
8. $9\overline{)1412} = 156\,R8$
9. $6\overline{)1486} = 247\,R4$
10. $4\overline{)3409} = 852\,R1$
11. $7\overline{)3934} = 562$
12. $3\overline{)1357} = 452\,R1$
13. $9\overline{)2115} = 235$
14. $5\overline{)1274} = 254\,R4$
15. $7\overline{)2252} = 321\,R5$

65

Division: Division Practice #15

Directions: Divide. Write answers in decimal form if required.

1. $7\overline{)6734} = 962$
2. $5\overline{)1436} = 287.2$
3. $4\overline{)1633} = 408.25$
4. $6\overline{)4431} = 738.5$
5. $9\overline{)4626} = 514$
6. $8\overline{)1964} = 245.5$
7. $5\overline{)3127} = 625.4$
8. $4\overline{)3254} = 813.5$
9. $3\overline{)1551} = 517$
10. $6\overline{)2325} = 387.5$
11. $5\overline{)2096} = 419.2$
12. $8\overline{)4898} = 612.25$
13. $9\overline{)2916} = 324$
14. $7\overline{)1582} = 226$
15. $8\overline{)6005} = 750.625$

66

Worksheet 1 (page 67)

Name: _____ Date: _____

Division: Division Practice #16

Directions: Divide. Write answers in remainder form if required.

1. 77)3858 = 50 R8
2. 45)1495 = 33 R10
3. 86)5504 = 64
4. 83)1418 = 17 R7
5. 29)1028 = 35 R13
6. 38)1243 = 32 R27
7. 95)2280 = 24
8. 85)2650 = 31 R15
9. 62)1521 = 24 R83
10. 69)4506 = 65 R21
11. 73)1145 = 15 R50
12. 41)2571 = 62 R29
13. 22)2761 = 125 R11
14. 55)1416 = 25 R41
15. 17)1622 = 95 R7

67

Worksheet 2 (page 68)

Name: _____ Date: _____

Division: Division Practice #17

Directions: Divide. Write answers in decimal form if required.

1. 96)2160 = 22.5
2. 68)1105 = 16.25
3. 92)5842 = 63.5
4. 24)1950 = 81.25
5. 30)2172 = 72.4
6. 55)4741 = 86.2
7. 34)3230 = 95
8. 26)3159 = 121.5
9. 25)7955 = 318.2
10. 36)3105 = 86.25
11. 41)5207 = 127
12. 82)7503 = 91.5
13. 22)8382 = 381
14. 18)2925 = 162.5
15. 32)2820 = 88.125

68

Worksheet 3 (page 69)

Name: _____ Date: _____

Division: Division Practice #18

Directions: Divide. Write answers in remainder form if required.

1. 214)4287 = 20 R7
2. 125)2875 = 23
3. 308)8016 = 26 R8
4. 197)6124 = 31 R17
5. 327)4920 = 15 R15
6. 254)6350 = 25
7. 318)6996 = 22
8. 149)4774 = 32 R6
9. 186)3373 = 18 R25
10. 241)5323 = 22 R21
11. 162)5684 = 35 R14
12. 229)9629 = 42 R11

69

Worksheet 4 (page 70)

Name: _____ Date: _____

Division: Division Practice #19

Directions: Divide. Write answers in decimal form if required.

1. 362)9593 = 26.5
2. 308)9625 = 31.25
3. 220)3861 = 17.55
4. 235)9729 = 41.4
5. 124)7750 = 62.5
6. 244)4697 = 19.25
7. 104)8658 = 83.25
8. 102)7395 = 72.5
9. 148)8769 = 59.25
10. 216)9531 = 44.125
11. 128)7184 = 56.125
12. 108)7695 = 71.25

70

Worksheet 5 (page 71)

Name: _____ Date: _____

Division: Division Word Problems #1

Directions: Write the division problem for each situation and then solve.

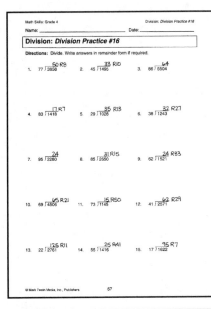

1. Three students work mowing lawns all summer. The students make $150 total.

   How much will each student receive if each gets the same amount? $50

2. A school has 175 students in it. There are seven grades in the school and each grade has the same number of students in it.

   How many students are in each grade?   25

3. A class of 25 students equally collected $2350 in a fund raiser.

   How much did each student raise? $94

4. A building is 150 feet high, and each floor is ten feet high.

   How many floors are in the building?   15

5. Ling and her brother are planning to drive to Alaska. It is 1500 miles to Alaska from their home. If each hour of driving they are able to go 50 miles, how many hours will it take to get to Alaska?   30

71

Worksheet 6 (page 72)

Name: _____ Date: _____

Division: Division Word Problems #2

Directions: Write the division problem for each situation and solve. Use remainders if necessary.

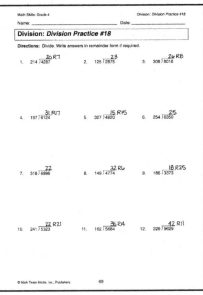

1. A store donated a box containing 365 cookies to a school fund-raising committee. If the students wrap the cookies eight in a package, how many packages will there be?   45 R5

2. Bill and his seven friends deliver papers in the morning. If the paper truck drops off 1045 papers, how many does each delivery person get?   130 R5

3. A computer's hard drive is 640,000,000 bytes in size. If each kilobyte is 1024 bytes, how many kilobytes are in the computer's hard drive?   625,000

4. A gas truck delivers 10,000 gallons of gas to a gas station. If the station has six tanks, how many gallons will go into each tank?   1666 R4

5. James estimates that he walks at least 258 blocks each week. If he walks six days a week, how many blocks will he walk each day?   43

72

Worksheet 7 (page 73)

Name: _____ Date: _____

Division: Division Word Problems #3

Directions: Write the division problem for each situation and solve. Use the decimal form if necessary.

1. Oliver has saved $456.25 over the past year. If there are 365 days in a year, how much did Oliver save each day? $1.25

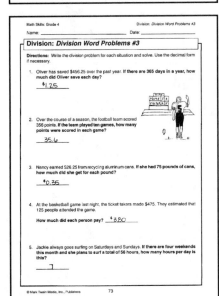

2. Over the course of a season, the football team scored 356 points. If the team played ten games, how many points were scored in each game?   35.6

3. Nancy earned $26.25 from recycling aluminum cans. If she had 75 pounds of cans, how much did she get for each pound? $0.35

4. At the basketball game last night, the ticket takers made $475. They estimated that 125 people attended the game.

   How much did each person pay? $3.80

5. Jackie always goes surfing on Saturdays and Sundays. If there are four weekends this month and she plans to surf a total of 56 hours, how many hours per day is this?   7

73

Worksheet 8 (page 74)

Name: _____ Date: _____

Division: Division Word Problems #4

Directions: Write the division problem for each situation and solve. Use the decimal form if necessary.

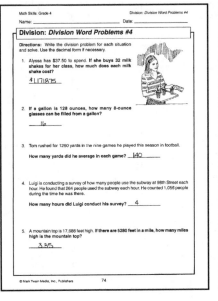

1. Alyssa has $37.50 to spend. If she buys 32 milk shakes for her class, how much does each milk shake cost? $1.171875

2. If a gallon is 128 ounces, how many 8-ounce glasses can be filled from a gallon?   16

3. Tom rushed for 1260 yards in the nine games he played this season in football.

   How many yards did he average in each game?   140

4. Luigi is conducting a survey of how many people use the subway at 98th Street each hour. He found that 264 people used the subway each hour. He counted 1,056 people during the time he was there.

   How many hours did Luigi conduct his survey?   4

5. A mountain top is 17,688 feet high. If there are 5280 feet in a mile, how many miles high is the mountain top?   3.35

74

Worksheet 9 (page 75)

Name: _____ Date: _____

Division: Division Word Problems #5

Directions: Write the division problem for each situation and solve. Use the decimal form if necessary.

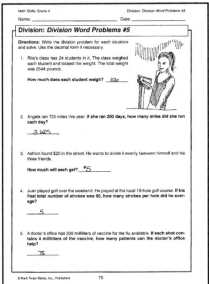

1. Rita's class has 24 students in it. The class weighed each student and totaled the weight. The total weight was 2544 pounds.

   How much does each student weigh?   106

2. Angela ran 725 miles this year. If she ran 200 days, how many miles did she run each day?   3.625

3. Ashton found $20 in the street. He wants to divide it evenly between himself and his three friends.

   How much will each get? $5

4. Juan played golf over the weekend. He played at the local 18-hole golf course. If his final total number of strokes was 90, how many strokes per hole did he average?   5

5. A doctor's office has 300 milliliters of vaccine for the flu available. If each shot contains 4 milliliters of the vaccine, how many patients can the doctor's office help?   75

75

Order of Operations: *Practice #1*

Directions: Find the answer using order of operations. Show each step.

1. 4 + 3 x 6
4 + 18 =
22

2. 5 - 1 x 2
5 - 2 =
3

3. 24 - 8 ÷ 4
16 + 4 =
20

4. 12 ÷ 4 + 7
3 + 7 =
10

5. 9 x 2 - 8
18 - 8 =
10

6. 16 ÷ 2 + 4
8 + 4 =
12

7. 12 - 6 ÷ 2
12 - 3 =
9

8. 15 - 6 ÷ 3
15 - 2 =
13

9. 16 + 9 x 2
16 + 18 =
34

10. 8 x 3 - 12
24 - 12 =
12

11. 18 ÷ 3 + 4
6 + 4 =
10

12. 6 x 4 + 4
24 + 4 =
28

13. 8 - 8 ÷ 4
8 - 2 =
6

14. 2 + 9 ÷ 3
2 + 3 =
5

15. 16 - 12 ÷ 2
16 - 6 =
10

Order of Operations: *Practice #2*

Directions: Find the answer using order of operations. Show each step.

1. (2 + 1) x (3 + 1)
3 x 4 =
12

2. (8 - 5) ÷ (6 - 2)
3 ÷ 4 =
0.75

3. (12 + 1) x (3 - 2)
13 x 1 =
13

4. (12 ÷ 4) + (15 ÷ 3)
3 + 5 =
8

5. (4 x 2) - (18 ÷ 6)
8 - 3 =
5

6. (16 ÷ 4) + (12 - 4)
4 + 8 =
12

7. (16 - 2) ÷ (10 - 3)
14 ÷ 7 =
2

8. (8 + 2) x (12 - 6)
10 x 6 =
60

9. (3 + 5) ÷ (5 - 3)
8 ÷ 2 =
4

10. (12 ÷ 2) - (4 x 1)
6 - 4 =
2

11. (20 ÷ 5) + (8 x 2)
4 + 16 =
20

12. (18 ÷ 3) - (12 ÷ 4)
6 - 3 =
3

13. (8 - 6) x (9 + 2)
2 x 11 =
22

14. (16 + 2) ÷ (12 - 4)
18 ÷ 8 =
2.25

15. (25 - 12) + (18 ÷ 3)
13 + 6 =
19

Order of Operations: *Assorted Word Problems #1*

Directions: Find the answers using addition, subtraction, multiplication, and division.

1. Spencer, Hunter, and Conner pooled their money and then split it so each had the same amount. Spencer had $25, Hunter had $23, and Conner had $24.

   How much would each have after they split up the total equally?
   _$24_
   (25 + 23 + 24) ÷ 3 = 72 ÷ 3 = 24

2. January and March had eight inches of rain each month. July and August had six inches of rain each month. If the remaining eight months had one inch each month, what is the total rainfall for the year?
   _36_
   (2 x 8) + (2 x 6) + (8 x 1) = 16 + 12 + 8 = 36

3. Jim bought three shirts at $10 each. He then purchased five shorts at $8 each.

   How much did Jim spend on clothes? _$70_
   (3 x 10) + (5 x 8) =
   30 + 40 = 70

4. Herb has two cases of pencils and an additional three packs that each contain six pencils. If a case holds 24 pencils, how many pencils does Herb have?
   _66_
   (2 x 24) + (3 x 6) =
   48 + 18 = 66

5. Megan saved up $4 a day for 25 days. She then bought three CD's for $15 each.

   How much money does Megan have left? _$55_
   (4 x 25) - (3 x 15) =
   100 - 45 = 55

Order of Operations: *Assorted Word Problems #2*

Directions: Find the answers using addition, subtraction, multiplication, and division.

1. A gallon contains 128 ounces and a half-gallon contains 64 ounces. Wendy's mother bought three gallons of punch and six half-gallons of juice

   How many total ounces of beverages did Wendy's mother buy?
   _768_
   (3 x 128) + (6 x 64) = 384 + 384 = 768

2. Becky has $700 in her checking account. She buys two jackets for $45 each and three pairs of shoes for $25 each. She then saves up $125.

   How much money does Becky have? _$660_
   (700 + 125) - [(2 x 45) + (3 x 25)] =
   825 - (90 + 75) = 825 - 165 = 660

3. April and Lexi have driven seven hours a day for six days. They slept five nights for eight hours each night. They spent another two hours a day for six days eating at different restaurants. They spent seven hours each day for six days sightseeing.

   How many total hours have they been gone? _136_
   (7 x 6) + (5 x 8) + (2 x 6) + (7 x 6) =
   42 + 40 + 12 + 42 = 136

4. Dale plays basketball. He scored five three-point baskets, 13 two-point baskets, and 11 free throws at one point each.

   How many points total did Dale score? _52_
   (5 x 3) + (13 x 2) + 11 =
   15 + 26 + 11 = 52

5. Andy is a runningback for his school's football team. In the first three games, Andy rushed for 125 yards in each game and caught passes for 85 yards in each game.

   How many yards total did Andy rush and receive in his first three games?
   _630_   (3 x 125) + (3 x 85) =
   375 + 255 = 630

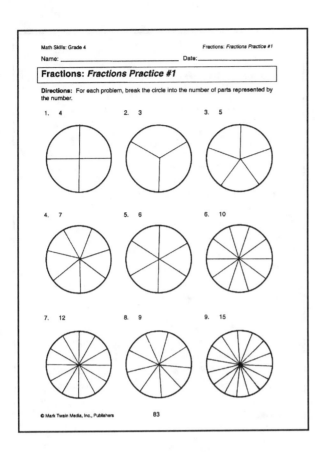

Math Skills: Grade 4   Fractions: Fractions Practice #1
Name: _____   Date: _____

Fractions: *Fractions Practice #1*

Directions: For each problem, break the circle into the number of parts represented by the number.

1. 4   2. 3   3. 5

4. 7   5. 6   6. 10

7. 12   8. 9   9. 15

© Mark Twain Media, Inc., Publishers   83

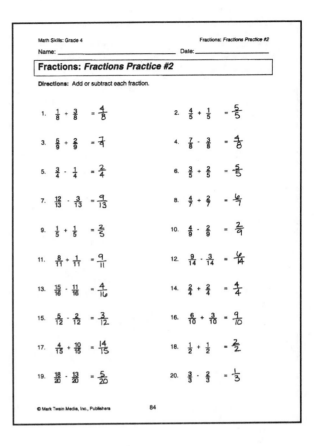

Math Skills: Grade 4   Fractions: Fractions Practice #2
Name: _____   Date: _____

Fractions: *Fractions Practice #2*

Directions: Add or subtract each fraction.

1. $\frac{1}{8} + \frac{3}{8} = \frac{4}{8}$ 2. $\frac{4}{5} + \frac{1}{5} = \frac{5}{5}$

3. $\frac{5}{9} + \frac{2}{9} = \frac{7}{9}$ 4. $\frac{7}{8} - \frac{3}{8} = \frac{4}{8}$

5. $\frac{3}{4} - \frac{1}{4} = \frac{2}{4}$ 6. $\frac{3}{5} + \frac{2}{5} = \frac{5}{5}$

7. $\frac{12}{13} - \frac{3}{13} = \frac{9}{13}$ 8. $\frac{4}{7} + \frac{2}{7} = \frac{6}{7}$

9. $\frac{1}{5} + \frac{1}{5} = \frac{2}{5}$ 10. $\frac{4}{9} - \frac{2}{9} = \frac{2}{9}$

11. $\frac{8}{11} + \frac{1}{11} = \frac{9}{11}$ 12. $\frac{9}{14} - \frac{3}{14} = \frac{6}{14}$

13. $\frac{15}{16} - \frac{11}{16} = \frac{4}{16}$ 14. $\frac{2}{4} + \frac{2}{4} = \frac{4}{4}$

15. $\frac{5}{12} - \frac{2}{12} = \frac{3}{12}$ 16. $\frac{6}{10} + \frac{3}{10} = \frac{9}{10}$

17. $\frac{4}{15} + \frac{10}{15} = \frac{14}{15}$ 18. $\frac{1}{2} + \frac{1}{2} = \frac{2}{2}$

19. $\frac{18}{20} - \frac{13}{20} = \frac{5}{20}$ 20. $\frac{3}{3} - \frac{2}{3} = \frac{1}{3}$

© Mark Twain Media, Inc., Publishers   84

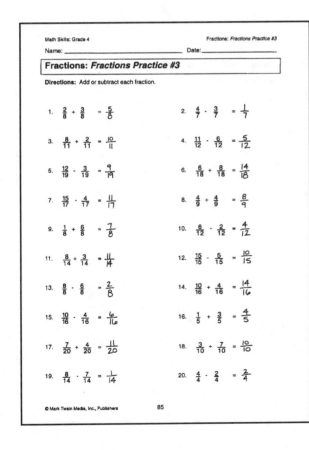

Math Skills: Grade 4   Fractions: Fractions Practice #3
Name: _____   Date: _____

Fractions: *Fractions Practice #3*

Directions: Add or subtract each fraction.

1. $\frac{2}{8} + \frac{3}{8} = \frac{5}{8}$ 2. $\frac{4}{7} - \frac{3}{7} = \frac{1}{7}$

3. $\frac{8}{11} + \frac{2}{11} = \frac{10}{11}$ 4. $\frac{11}{12} - \frac{6}{12} = \frac{5}{12}$

5. $\frac{12}{19} - \frac{3}{19} = \frac{9}{19}$ 6. $\frac{6}{18} + \frac{8}{18} = \frac{14}{18}$

7. $\frac{15}{17} - \frac{4}{17} = \frac{11}{17}$ 8. $\frac{4}{9} + \frac{4}{9} = \frac{8}{9}$

9. $\frac{1}{8} + \frac{6}{8} = \frac{7}{8}$ 10. $\frac{6}{12} - \frac{2}{12} = \frac{4}{12}$

11. $\frac{8}{14} + \frac{3}{14} = \frac{11}{14}$ 12. $\frac{15}{15} - \frac{5}{15} = \frac{10}{15}$

13. $\frac{8}{8} - \frac{6}{8} = \frac{2}{8}$ 14. $\frac{10}{16} + \frac{4}{16} = \frac{14}{16}$

15. $\frac{10}{16} - \frac{4}{16} = \frac{6}{16}$ 16. $\frac{1}{5} + \frac{3}{5} = \frac{4}{5}$

17. $\frac{7}{20} + \frac{4}{20} = \frac{11}{20}$ 18. $\frac{3}{10} + \frac{7}{10} = \frac{10}{10}$

19. $\frac{8}{14} - \frac{7}{14} = \frac{1}{14}$ 20. $\frac{4}{4} - \frac{2}{4} = \frac{2}{4}$

© Mark Twain Media, Inc., Publishers   85

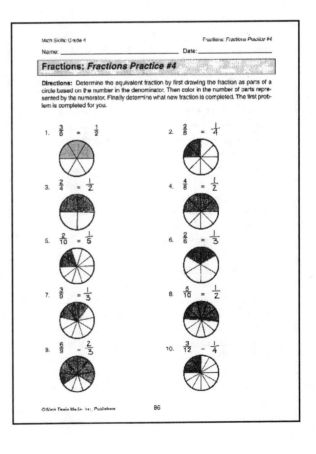

Math Skills: Grade 4   Fractions: Fractions Practice #4
Name: _____   Date: _____

Fractions: *Fractions Practice #4*

Directions: Determine the equivalent fraction by first drawing the fraction as parts of a circle based on the number in the denominator. Then color in the number of parts represented by the numerator. Finally determine what new fraction is completed. The first problem is completed for you.

1. $\frac{3}{6} = \frac{1}{2}$ 2. $\frac{2}{8} = \frac{1}{4}$

3. $\frac{2}{4} = \frac{1}{2}$ 4. $\frac{4}{8} = \frac{1}{2}$

5. $\frac{2}{10} = \frac{1}{5}$ 6. $\frac{2}{6} = \frac{1}{3}$

7. $\frac{3}{9} = \frac{1}{3}$ 8. $\frac{5}{10} = \frac{1}{2}$

9. $\frac{6}{9} = \frac{2}{3}$ 10. $\frac{3}{12} = \frac{1}{4}$

© Mark Twain Media, Inc., Publishers   86

Geometry: Triangles Practice #1

Geometry: *Triangles Practice #1*

Directions: Classify each triangle by its angles and side lengths.

1. right, scalene
2. acute, scalene
3. obtuse, isosceles
4. acute, scalene
5. acute, isosceles
6. right, isosceles
7. obtuse, isosceles
8. obtuse, scalene
9. acute, equilateral

© Mark Twain Media, Inc., Publishers   88

Geometry: *Triangles Practice #2*

Directions: Answer the following as sometimes, always, or never.

1. Acute triangles are right triangles. — never
2. Acute triangles are obtuse triangles. — never
3. Acute triangles are scalene triangles. — sometimes
4. Acute triangles are isosceles triangles. — sometimes
5. Acute triangles are equilateral triangles. — sometimes
6. Equilateral triangles are scalene triangles. — never
7. Equilateral triangles are isosceles triangles. — always
8. Equilateral triangles are acute triangles. — always
9. Equilateral triangles are obtuse triangles. — never
10. Equilateral triangles are right triangles. — never
11. Obtuse triangles are right triangles. — never
12. Obtuse triangles are acute triangles. — never
13. Obtuse triangles are scalene triangles. — sometimes
14. Obtuse triangles are equilateral triangles. — never
15. Obtuse triangles are isosceles triangles. — sometimes
16. Isosceles triangles are scalene triangles. — never
17. Isosceles triangles are obtuse triangles. — sometimes
18. Isosceles triangles are equilateral triangles. — sometimes
19. Isosceles triangles are acute triangles. — sometimes
20. Isosceles triangles are right triangles. — sometimes

© Mark Twain Media, Inc., Publishers   89

Geometry: *Triangles Practice #2* (Continued)

Directions: Answer the following as sometimes, always, or never.

21. Right triangles are scalene triangles. — sometimes
22. Right triangles are acute triangles. — never
23. Right triangles are obtuse triangles. — never
24. Right triangles are isosceles triangles. — sometimes
25. Right triangles are equilateral triangles. — never
26. Scalene triangles are acute triangles. — sometimes
27. Scalene triangles are obtuse triangles. — sometimes
28. Scalene triangles are right triangles. — sometimes
29. Scalene triangles are isosceles triangles. — never
30. Scalene triangles are equilateral triangles. — never

Directions: Answer the following questions.

1. Why are equilateral triangles always acute triangles? Each angle in an equilateral triangle is exactly 60° and therefore each angle is acute.
2. Why are acute triangles never right triangles? Acute means that each angle is less than 90°. Right means that one angle is exactly 90°.
3. Why are equilateral triangles always isosceles triangles? Isosceles triangles must have at least two sides of equal measure. Equilateral triangles have all three sides equal and therefore at least two are equal.
4. Why are scalene triangles never isosceles triangles? Scalene triangles have no sides with equal length while isosceles must have at least two sides with equal length.

© Mark Twain Media, Inc., Publishers   90

Geometry: *Quadrilaterals Practice #1*

Directions: Match the term with the correct shape. Answers may be used more than once.

A,B,C,D,E,F 1. Quadrilateral   A.   B.   C.
E 2. Trapezoid
A, B, C, D 3. Parallelogram
A, D 4. Rectangle   D.   E.   F.
C 5. Rhombus
D 6. Square

Directions: Fill in the missing classifications using the following terms: **Square, Rhombus, Rectangle, Parallelogram,** and **Trapezoid.**

Quadrilateral

One pair of sides parallel — trapezoid

Both pairs of sides parallel — parallelogram

Four 90° angles — rectangle

Four equal sides — rhombus

Four equal sides and 90° angles — square

Key:

Arrows pointing down mean sometimes.

Arrows pointing up mean always.

© Mark Twain Media, Inc., Publishers   93

Math Skills: Grade 4   Geometry: Quadrilaterals Practice #2

Name: _____ Date: _____

Geometry: Quadrilaterals Practice #2

Directions: Use the quadrilateral diagram below to answer the questions as always, sometimes, or never.

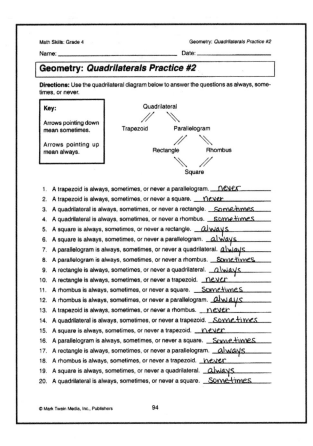

Key:

Arrows pointing down mean sometimes.

Arrows pointing up mean always.

1. A trapezoid is always, sometimes, or never a parallelogram. _never_
2. A trapezoid is always, sometimes, or never a square. _never_
3. A quadrilateral is always, sometimes, or never a rectangle. _sometimes_
4. A quadrilateral is always, sometimes, or never a rhombus. _sometimes_
5. A square is always, sometimes, or never a rectangle. _always_
6. A square is always, sometimes, or never a parallelogram. _always_
7. A parallelogram is always, sometimes, or never a quadrilateral. _always_
8. A parallelogram is always, sometimes, or never a rhombus. _sometimes_
9. A rectangle is always, sometimes, or never a quadrilateral. _always_
10. A rectangle is always, sometimes, or never a trapezoid. _never_
11. A rhombus is always, sometimes, or never a square. _sometimes_
12. A rhombus is always, sometimes, or never a parallelogram. _always_
13. A trapezoid is always, sometimes, or never a rhombus. _never_
14. A quadrilateral is always, sometimes, or never a trapezoid. _sometimes_
15. A square is always, sometimes, or never a trapezoid. _never_
16. A parallelogram is always, sometimes, or never a square. _sometimes_
17. A rectangle is always, sometimes, or never a parallelogram. _always_
18. A rhombus is always, sometimes, or never a trapezoid. _never_
19. A square is always, sometimes, or never a quadrilateral. _always_
20. A quadrilateral is always, sometimes, or never a square. _Sometimes_

© Mark Twain Media, Inc., Publishers   94

Math Skills: Grade 4   Geometry: Three-Dimensional Figures Practice #1

Name: _____ Date: _____

Geometry: Three-Dimensional Figures Practice #1

Directions: Match the terms with the correct figures.

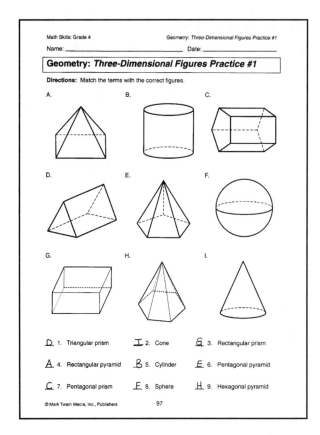

D 1. Triangular prism   I 2. Cone   G 3. Rectangular prism

A 4. Rectangular pyramid   B 5. Cylinder   E 6. Pentagonal pyramid

C 7. Pentagonal prism   F 8. Sphere   H 9. Hexagonal pyramid

© Mark Twain Media, Inc., Publishers   97

Math Skills: Grade 4   Geometry: Three-Dimensional Figures Practice #2

Name: _____ Date: _____

Geometry: Three-Dimensional Figures Practice #2

Directions: Write out the names of the various shapes given the name of the bases.

Base Shape	Pyramid	Prism
1. Octagon (8 sides)	Octagonal Pyramid	Octagonal Prism
2. Decagon (10 sides)	Decagonal Pyramid	Decagonal Prism
3. Heptagon (7 sides)	Heptagonal Pyramid	Heptagonal Prism
4. Nonagon (9 sides)	Nonagonal Pyramid	Nonagonal Prism
5. Dodecagon (12 sides)	Dodecagonal Pyramid	Dodecagonal Prism
6. Icosagon (20 sides)	Icosagonal Pyramid	Icosagonal Prism
7. Undecagon (11 sides)	Undecagonal Pyramid	Undecagonal Prism

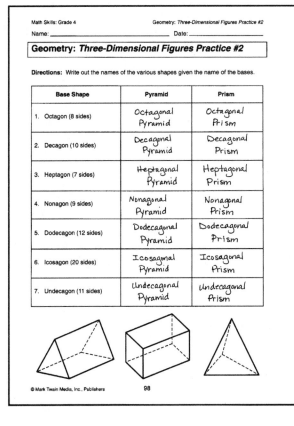

© Mark Twain Media, Inc., Publishers   98

Math Skills: Grade 4   Metrics: Metric Practice #1

Name: _____ Date: _____

Metrics: Metric Practice #1

Directions: Measure the following bold lines and give the metric measure in decimeters, centimeters, and millimeters.

1. Decimeters: _1 dm_   Centimeters: _10 cm_   Millimeters: _100 mm_

2. Decimeters: _0.5 dm_   Centimeters: _5 cm_   Millimeters: _50 mm_

3. Decimeters: _0.1 dm_   Centimeters: _1 cm_   Millimeters: _10 mm_

4. Decimeters: _0.15 dm_   Centimeters: _1.5 cm_   Millimeters: _15 mm_

5. Decimeters: _1.25 dm_   Centimeters: _12.5 cm_   Millimeters: _125 mm_

Directions: Answer the following questions.

1. How many millimeters (mm) are in a meter (m)? _1000 mm_

2. How many millimeters (mm) are in a decimeter (dm)? _100 mm_

3. How many millimeters (mm) are in a centimeter (cm)? _10 mm_

4. How many grams (g) are in a kilogram (kg)? _1000 g_

5. How many grams (g) are in a hectogram (hg)? _100 g_

6. How many grams (g) are in a decagram (dag)? _10 g_

© Mark Twain Media, Inc., Publishers   101

Teacher Notes